Volume 1

A-BOMB

ANILINE DYE

THE NEW
how it works

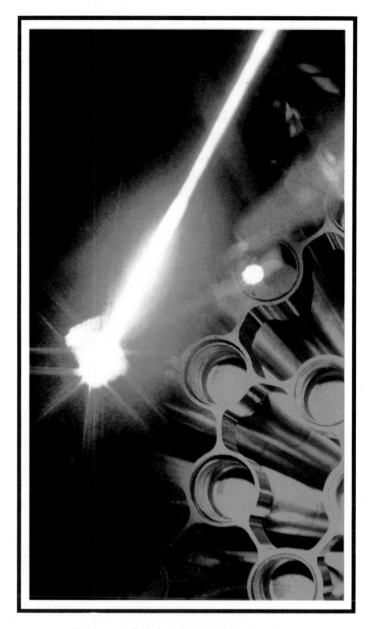

*Experimental nuclear fusion reactors use the laser
and highly ionized plasma. Gas-cooled fusion
reactor fuel assembly is at right.*
Photo: Paul Brierley

THE *NEW* ILLUSTRATED

Science
and
Invention

ENCYCLOPEDIA

H. S. STUTTMAN INC. PUBLISHERS · WESTPORT, CONNECTICUT 06889

Introduction

In this twentieth century, the world has witnessed a quickening of the pace of technological advancement that is unprecedented in recorded human history. In its earliest years, for example, the Age of Flight dawned with the first brief hops in machines such as the Wright brothers' Flyer. Barely three generations later, travelers can fly at supersonic speeds, spacecraft have taken astronauts to the Moon and others, unmanned, are exploring planets in outer space.

Within a much briefer period, the first room-sized electronic computers gave way to smaller but extraordinarily faster transistorized machines. These in turn were superseded by the powerful microelectronic brains that are crucial to modern communications, commerce, weaponry, and manufacturing processes.

Much of this burgeoning technology was triggered by breakthroughs in knowledge – such as the chemical process for preparing nitrogen for fertilizers and explosives – but most of it is based on the inventions of pioneering experimenters and

Helicopter/Vol. 9

Published by H. S. STUTTMAN INC.
Westport, Connecticut 06889
© Marshall Cavendish Limited 1987, 1989

the knowledge amassed by scientists, engineers, and technologists throughout the ages.

This wealth of information has been classified, researched and brought together in 26 volumes in the New Illustrated Science and Invention Encyclopedia: HOW IT WORKS. These extensively illustrated volumes have been thoroughly revised to include the latest scientific concepts, developments and inventions, and form a valuable, lasting reference library for both the technically informed and nonspecialist reader.

The keystones of the New Illustrated Science and Invention Encyclopedia are twofold: first, it has an easily understandable, yet detailed and authoritative, text written by experts who understand well the importance of communicating detailed technical information in a lucid, well-organized style that makes it easily assimilated by a broad spectrum of readers. Not surprisingly, therefore, this work will be welcomed by the interested general reader, the nonspecialist, the middle-to-upper grade science or engineering student, and even the technical expert, as the

cornerstone of a home or office library.

Second, the encyclopedia features extensive use of detailed informative color photographs and drawings that complement the text and make the entire work a valuable learning aid. To find out the working principle of a system, or the way a machine or process works, the New Illustrated Science and Invention Encyclopedia is the source to consult. Here is the place to discover the origins of atomic theory, learn about scientific concepts – such as the modern theories on gravitation and relativity, find out about the drifting continents, and see how a laser generates energy to "weld" tissue in the eye, start nuclear fusion, or destroy a satellite in deep space.

The New Illustrated Science and Invention Encyclopedia provides answers to everyday questions, too. How, for example, does instant picture film differ from the image on your television screen? What are the treatments for cancer? Are superplastics any better than metals? And what will be used to fuel industry when the oil runs out? Whatever your field of work or study, this reference source is the perfect companion to keep you abreast of the rapidly advancing, increasingly technical world we live in today.

Editorial Staff

First edition

Executive Editor	Donald Clarke
Science Education Consultant	Charles La Rue
Originating Editor	Ralph Hancock

Revision Staff

Editor	Mark K. Dartford
Executive Editors	Trevor Morris
	Lloyd Lindo
Designers	Keith Vollans
	Janina Samoles
Photo Resource Consultant	Julia Wood

A full list of staff credits and contributors will be found in Volume 26.

Reader's Guide

This newly revised and updated HOW IT WORKS contains a number of features designed to make it easier to use than ever before.

Arrangement
Volumes 1–23 cover over 1000 main subject entries in strict alphabetical order.

Chemical and biological warfare, therefore, precedes **Chemistry.** Headings containing more than one word are alphabetized as if they were one word up to the punctuation mark. Words appearing in parenthesis, however, are not considered part of the heading for purposes of alphabetization.

> Thus:
> **Cable, power**
> **Cable, submarine**
> **Cable railway**

Each volume is prefaced with a contents list and contains an average of 40 entries, varying in length from one to eight complete pages. Certain articles are developed further with a "Frontiers of Science" feature. These range from astrophysics to drug therapy, and present a comprehensive review of a challenging new aspect of the related alphabetical entry. In Volume One the "Adhesive: Frontiers" feature describes how surgeons are using superglue instead of stitches to join human tissue. In addition, many entries contain "Fact File" boxes. In these separate sections you will find from two to four historical, unusual or improbable items of fascinating fact. In "Battery" one of the Fact File items tells how in the U.S. at the turn of the century battery-operated cars outnumbered cars with gasoline engines.

Volume 24 presents 100 biographies of famous scientists and inventors. From Sir John Adams to Vladimir Kosma Zworykin, each biography recounts the life and efforts of the men and women who shaped modern science and technology.

Volume 25 provides a chronological listing of more than 70 of the most significant scientific inventions and discoveries, from the wheel to the optical computer.

Volume 26 includes an illustrated "Milestones of Science" grouped chronologically, and a "Glossary" of more than 2000 scientific and technical terms. This is followed by two indexes: the first being thematic, with entries arranged under 88 classifications (for example: Agriculture, Military Technology, Telecommunications), and finally a regular A–Z index with over 8000 entries. Both indexes give page and volume number references.

Reference facilities
To find entries rapidly, there is a running head next to the page number at the top of every page throughout volumes 1–24.

Throughout the text *italics* are used to highlight out-of-the-ordinary terms explained in the surrounding copy; for example: "the air-cooled *radial* engine, in which static cylinders were arranged in a circle, and cooled by the backwash of the propeller."

SMALL CAPITAL LETTERS signify one of the 2000 technical terms given a fuller explanation in the Glossary section in Volume 26. For example: "Antimatter, if it existed anywhere in the universe, would be composed exclusively of ANTIPARTICLES."

All entries are followed by an alphabetical list of references, allowing a reader to find further information about a subject without resorting to the index. For example: Anemometer – See also: Aerodynamics; Dynamo; Fluidics; Pitot tube; Wind tunnel.

Weights & Measurements
Weights and measures are given in both standard and (in parentheses) metric equivalents – except where convention, as in the case of some heavy artillery, demands a universal unit.

Contents of the Set

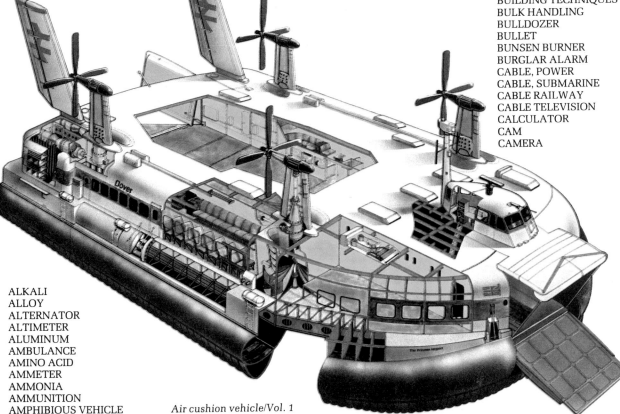

Air cushion vehicle/Vol. 1

Dragster/Vol. 6

Crane/Vol. 5

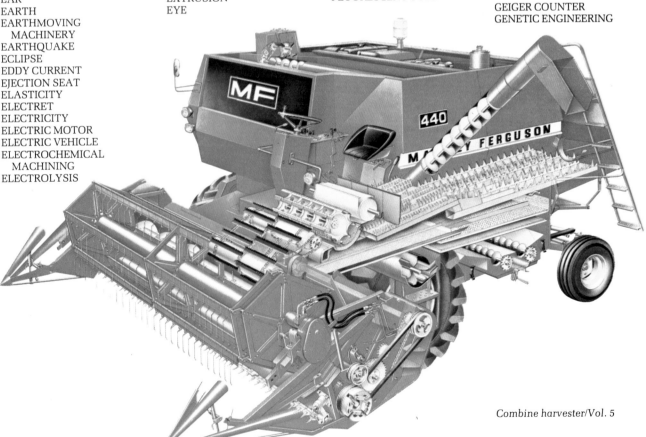

Combine harvester/Vol. 5

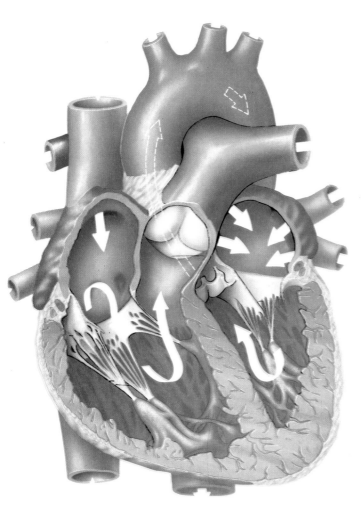

Heart-lung machine/Vol. 9

*Map-making techniques/
   Vol. 11*

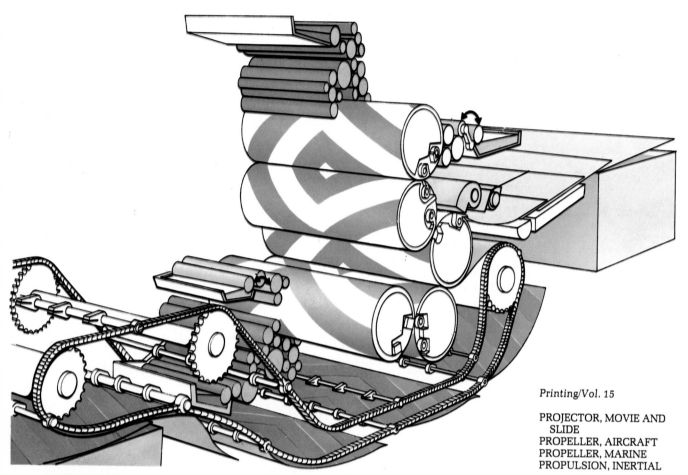

Pest control/Vol. 14

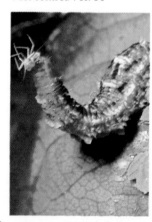

Space Shuttle/Vol. 18

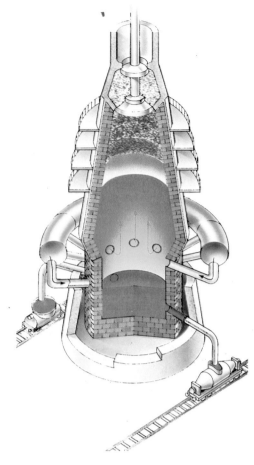

Steel manufacture/Vol. 19

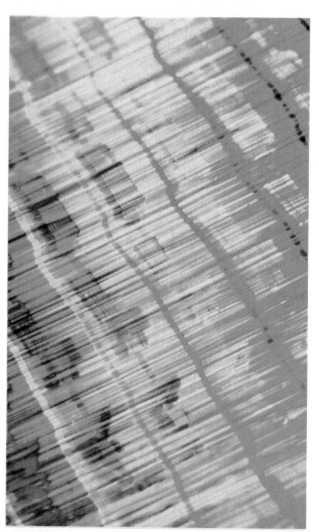

Special effect/Vol. 19

Contents

Volume 1

A-bomb

The A-bomb, or atomic bomb, has been used only twice in war, at Hiroshima and Nagasaki, and both times it has totally destroyed a large city in a single explosion.

Strictly speaking, the term atomic bomb includes the H-bomb, which also uses atomic power. But in general usage, atomic bomb is reserved for earlier weapons that work by nuclear fission, that is, splitting atoms. The hydrogen bomb works by nuclear fusion – joining small atoms together to make larger ones. Both fission and fusion release huge amounts of energy and radioactivity.

Nuclear fission

The huge power of an atomic bomb comes from the forces holding each individual ATOM of a substance together. These forces act over tiny distances deep within the atom itself. Every atom of every substance that exists is held together by them. The energy released by splitting one atom is tiny, but there are so many billion atoms in even the smallest piece of material that a great deal of power can be released from large quantities.

Most naturally occurring ELEMENTS (pure substances) have very stable atoms which are impossible to split except by using such techniques as

Below and right: The initial explosion of an air burst atomic bomb releases about 85 per cent of its energy as intense heat, followed by a supersonic shock wave. 50 per cent of the bomb's output is felt as a highly destructive high-pressure air blast, followed by a low-pressure wave of equal intensity.

DEVELOPMENT OF AN AIR-BURST ATOMIC EXPLOSION

ENERGY RELEASED

- 5% initial radiation
- 10% residual radiation
- 35% heat
- 50% blast

Fission products injected into atmosphere

Mushroom cloud

Mushroom stem

Detonation

Fireball develops

Blast wave

Fireball

Mach wave

Reflected shock front

Formation of mushroom cloud

Winds

U–235 BOMB LITTLE BOY

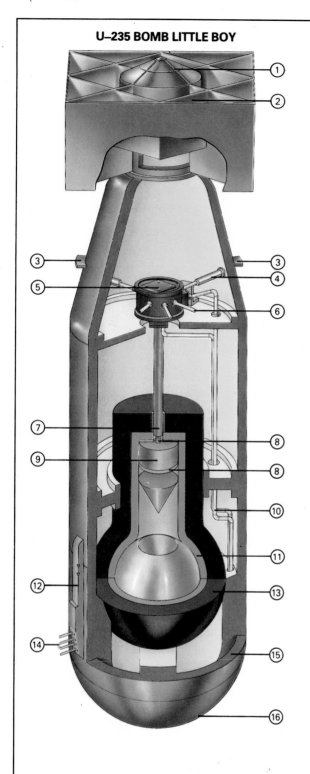

1 Tail cone	9 Conventional explosive charge
2 Stabilizing tail fins	10 Electronic conduits and fusing circuits
3 Airstream deflectors	11 Neutron reflector
4 Air inlet tube	12 Battery stores
5 Air pressure detonator	13 Cast bomb casing
6 Pressure sensors	14 Telemetry monitoring probes
7 Detonating head	15 Lead shield container
8 Packing	16 Fuzes

bombarding them in a particle accelerator. But there is one natural element whose atoms can be split comparatively easily: this is the metal uranium. Its special property comes from the very huge size of its atoms; they are too big to be held together firmly.

Atoms are (for practical purposes) made up of three kinds of subatomic particles, tiny fragments of matter which are the same in all atoms of all elements. These are PROTONS and NEUTRONS which cluster together to form the NUCLEUS, or central mass, of the atom, and ELECTRONS, which spin in orbits around the nucleus. The lighter the element, the fewer the subatomic particles in its atoms.

Uranium is an extremely heavy metal, heavier than gold, and it has the largest atoms of any natural element. Moreover, the atoms have far more neutrons than protons, which does not make them easier to split, but does have an important bearing on the amount of energy they release during an explosion.

There are two ISOTOPES of uranium: an isotope is a form of an element distinguished by the number of neutrons in its atom. Natural uranium consists mostly of the isotope U-238, which has 92 protons and 146 neutrons (92+146=238). But mixed in with this is about 0.6 per cent of the other isotope, U-235, which has the same number of protons but only 143 neutrons. This isotope, unlike U-238, is fissionable (its atoms can be split), and so it is the one used for making bombs.

Both isotopes of uranium, and certain other heavy elements, are naturally radioactive, that is, their big, unstable atoms slowly disintegrate in the course of time. The spare neutrons are thrown off, and so are various other particles. Left to themselves, uranium atoms eventually lose so many particles that they turn into a completely different element, the metal lead. This change takes many thousand years before a measurable number of atoms have turned to lead.

Atoms of U-235 can be made to break up much faster than this in a chain reaction. Instead of disintegrating slowly by themselves, the atoms are forcibly split by neutrons forcing their way into the nucleus. A U-235 atom is so unstable that a blow from a single neutron is enough to split it. Usually it splits into two smaller atoms of different elements, such as barium and krypton.

When a U-235 atom splits it gives off energy in the form of heat and GAMMA RADIATION, the most powerful form of radioactivity and the one which is most harmful to life. It also gives off two or three of its

Left: A cutaway view of the U–235 Little Boy atomic bomb that was dropped on Hiroshima, Japan in August 1945. It was a uranium gun-type bomb and killed over 80,000 people.

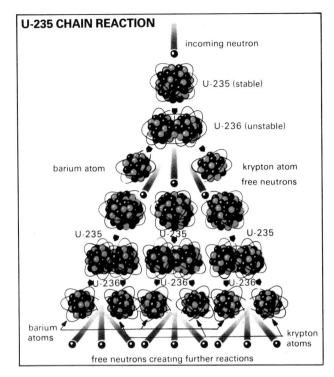

U-235 CHAIN REACTION

incoming neutron

U-235 (stable)

U-236 (unstable)

barium atom

krypton atom

free neutrons

U-235 U-235 U-235

U-236 U-236 U-236

barium atoms

krypton atoms

free neutrons creating further reactions

Above: A single neutron only is needed to start the chain reaction that produces the atomic explosion.

spare neutrons, which are not needed to make the barium and krypton atoms. These fly out with sufficient force to split other atoms if they hit them.

In theory, it is necessary to split only one U-235 atom, for the neutrons from this will split other atoms, which in turn will split more, and so on. This is why the reaction is called a chain reaction. It happens with great speed; all the atoms split within a millionth of a second.

In practice, it is not quite so simple to start a nuclear explosion. There has to be a certain weight of U-235 present before the chain reaction will sustain itself. If there is less than this amount there will be too few atoms to insure that neutrons from every atom that splits will hit other atoms.

The minimum amount is known as the CRITICAL MASS. The theoretical critical mass is about 2 lb (1 kg) of pure U-235. In practice, however, the degree of purity is so low that 110 lb (50 kg) – the effective critical mass – is required in order to sustain a chain reaction.

Uranium is not the only material used for making A-bombs. Another material is the element plutonium, in its isotope Pu-239. Plutonium is not

Below: August 6, 1945 Hiroshima – completely devastated after the bomb detonated over the city.

found naturally (except in minute traces) and is always made from uranium. This can be done by putting U-238 in a nuclear reactor. After a while, the intense radioactivity causes it to pick up the extra particles, so that more and more of its atoms turn into plutonium.

Plutonium will not start a fast chain reaction by itself, but this difficulty is overcome by having a neutron source, a highly radioactive material that gives off neutrons faster than the plutonium itself.

Mechanism of the bomb

A bomb cannot be made simply by putting a piece of uranium larger than critical mass into a casing, because this would cause it to go off immediately. Instead, two or more pieces are inserted a safe distance apart and assembled, or shot together, to start a chain reaction.

The simplest possible atomic bomb is one of the type dropped on Hiroshima. It is known as a gun-type bomb since it actually contains a type of gun. At one end of the barrel there is a target, a piece of U-235 slightly smaller than critical mass and shaped like a sphere with a conical wedge removed from it to form a tapering gap.

At the other end of the barrel there is another, smaller, piece of U-235 in the shape of a cone with its apex pointing towards the gap in the target. It is the exact shape of the piece missing from the sphere. Together, the two pieces exceed the critical mass.

The smaller piece is backed by a charge of ordinary HIGH EXPLOSIVE. When this is set off, the cone is shot into the sphere and the force of impact welds the two pieces together solidly. The explosion follows instantly.

Plutonium bombs are slightly more sophisticated. Plutonium is even more easily fissionable than U-235, and its critical mass is lower: 35.2 lb (16 kg) for pure Pu-239.

The mass can be reduced further, to 22 lb (10 kg), by making a sphere of this weight of plutonium and surrounding it with nonfissionable U-238, which reflects neutrons back into the center of the sphere and minimizes loss to the outside.

Plutonium cannot be exploded so easily by a gun-type device. It has to be assembled with much greater speed or it will not explode properly.

Plutonium is therefore assembled by a technique known as IMPLOSION. A number of wedge-shaped pieces of plutonium, which together will build up into a sphere, are arranged at equal intervals around a neutron source. Explosive charges of exactly equal weight are placed behind each wedge and all are detonated together. The wedges shoot towards the centre and touch each other at the same moment. This technique was used for the second American atomic bomb, which was dropped on the city of Nagasaki.

• FACT FILE •

- The flash of the Hiroshima bomb was so intense that it discolored concrete and sealed the surface of granite, leaving in many places prints of the shadows cast by the light of the explosion. By triangulating these shadows with the objects that had cast them, Japanese scientists were able to pinpoint the exact center of the blast. Some of the shadows were of people.

- Today's nuclear warheads are smaller and more powerful than ever before, in order to maximize the efficiency of the delivery system. At the outset of the Manhattan Project, Albert Einstein was one of the scientists who forecast that an A-Bomb would have to be so large and heavy that it would need a ship to deliver it to its target.

- A one-megaton bomb detonated at ground zero would produce a crater 200 feet deep and a thousand feet across. Nuclear shelters have been designed both for private purchase and national use. Sweden and Switzerland have laid plans to shelter their entire populations.

Above: A public shelter in Switzerland. The Swiss aim to have shelters capable of withstanding nuclear bombardment for everyone by about the year 2000.

See also: Atom and molecule; Bomb; Electromagnetic radiation; Hydrogen bomb; Nuclear reactor; Radioactivity; Space weapon.

Abrasive

The abrading effect is produced almost entirely by the simple physical process of the harder substance shearing or fracturing small chips off the workpiece to smooth it.

Abrasives are used in three main ways. One is to use the abrasive material directly on a substance: sharpening a knife on a grinding wheel is an example of this. Another is to coat another substance, such as a piece of paper, cloth or rubber on a metal disc, with granules of abrasive material, and use this as a tool; sandpaper is the commonest application of this technique. The third method is sandblasting or gritblasting, where a powerful stream of air containing abrasive particles is directed at an object to abrade its surface.

Apart from their use in sharpening-stones and grinding wheels, direct-action abrasives are also used in powder form. Most domestic cleaning agents (except soap and washing powder) contain abrasives, which are generally silica, pumice or aluminum oxide ground to a very fine powder. The chemical action of the cleaning agent is helped by the abrasive, and the two substances clean faster than either would alone.

Toothpaste also contains a mild abrasive, which is generally finely powdered chalk. Old-fashioned tooth powder often contained powdered pumice or silica, which wore the enamel off the teeth in a short time, but manufacturers now claim that the cleaning action of their product is mostly chemical.

Most abrasives used in industry are applied indirectly by being stuck to a backing. This saves expense because less abrasive is used.

The simplest type of coated abrasive material is sandpaper, which is made by simply glueing granules of abrasive material to a sheet of paper.

Abrasive papers are made in a vast range of types, and have many uses. One unusual application is in the printing industry, where a sheet of paper to be printed on both sides is laid on a sheet of abrasive paper called tympan (abrasive side up) while the second side is printed. In this way, the printed side can rest on the abrasive points, which hold it steady and prevent the wet ink from smearing.

Abrasive-coated belts are used in many industrial sanding machines. These may be made of extra strong paper, or else a fine, strong cloth such as linen or gaberdine is used.

Gritblasting with a machine is a versatile technique. It has the important feature that the workpiece is abraded more or less evenly all over the surface that faces the blast. It is used for cleaning metal objects thoroughly before they are electroplated – electro-plating will not stick to dirt or corrosion. It is also used for incising patterns on

Top: Steelworker abrading the joins in a length of steel piping with a high-speed angle grinder.
Above: One type of abrasive is produced by fusing bauxite in an electric furnace.

plate glass. The area of the glass that is to be left smooth is protected with a tough paper stencil that is only partly eaten away by the blasting. This technique has replaced the older one of etching patterns on glass with hydrofluoric acid.

Types of abrasive material
Abrasive materials may be either natural or synthetic. Traditional abrasives are all natural, and the synthetic ones are a fairly recent innovation.

The oldest abrasive of all is sand, which was used for polishing stone weapons as early as 25,000 BC.

Other abrasive materials in use from early times include garnet (a hard, glasslike gemstone), emery,

Above: Industrial abrasion techniques are designed to toughen as well as finish steel products.
Left: High-speed finishing of wood or even metal can be achieved by choosing the correct grade of hardness. In this case, the abrading surface is attached to the revolving drum, and the surface of the workpiece to be ground is applied by hand.

pumice, and silica (silicon dioxide) which occurs in various forms as quartz, flint and agate. In the Middle Ages, grinding wheels of quartz and flint fragments naturally bonded together in rock were used. Gemstones were lapped or polished by the use of emery or sandstone powder rubbed on with metal plates.

Sandpaper was discovered slightly later, and was followed by emery paper and cloth, which are finer grained and longer lasting, and corundum, discovered in 1825.

The most important step in the development of synthetic abrasives was made in 1891, when Edward Acheson first produced crystals of silicon carbide. This material was called Carborundum, and has been one of the most versatile synthetic abrasives. The crystals, which can be made in any required degree of fineness, can be bonded together in a solid block or used for coating metal discs or belts for use in machine tools such as sanders.

Other, more recent developments include aluminum oxide, a synthetic form of corundum, silicon carbide and synthetic diamonds. These have not ousted natural diamonds, however, which are still better for bonding on to the steel discs which are used for cutting stone and concrete. Synthetic diamonds are used mainly for cutting and shaping other very hard substances, such as tungsten carbide. They are produced from carbon at high temperature and pressure, as are natural ones.

Already, improvements in abrasive technology have displaced some intermediate stages in the shaping and finishing of materials. As new wonder materials are developed to meet the needs of modern industry, this trend will continue and new super-abrasives will be required. In meeting this need, modern technology might not be able to improve on all the properties to be found in diamond but it can certainly attain a close second best.

See also: Diamond; Electrochemical machining; Sand and shot blasting; Silicon; Toothpaste.

Accelerometer

An accelerometer is an instrument for measuring acceleration. There are two types, one for measuring *linear* (straight-line) accelerations, the other for measuring *angular* (twisting) accelerations.

Accelerometers may also be used to measure deceleration, such as the braking of a car. They are much used in the motor industry both to measure the forward acceleration and deceleration of a car, and to measure the sideways and up-and-down accelerations caused by cornering and bumpy roads.

Other uses include testing the strength of safety belts (by measuring the deceleration force at which they break when carrying a known load) and studying vibrations in the hulls of ships and the wingtips of aircraft. They are also important components of inertial guidance systems.

The linear accelerometer usually contains a body of known mass attached to a coil spring and free to move only along the axis of the spring, which is a straight line down the middle of the coil. This line is called the sensitive axis of the accelerometer. In order to measure the acceleration of any moving object, the axis must be placed in line with the direction of movement.

The tension of the spring and the weight of the

body on its end are adjusted so that when a known force is applied to the accelerometer along the sensitive axis, the body moves a known distance along the spring. The body is either connected to a dial, or its movement is detected electronically.

The dial is calibrated by placing the accelerometer on a body of known acceleration and marking the position of the indicator. If this is repeated with various known accelerations, the marks will provide enough information to allow the rest of the scale to be filled in.

Linear acceleration can be measured in various units. Moderate forces are generally measured in units such as feet or meters per second per second, written as ft/s^2 or ft^{-2}, which is the number of feet per second a body adds to its speed every second. Higher forces are generally measured in g units, that is, how many times greater they are than the force of gravity. One g, the acceleration of an object falling freely to the ground, is $32 \, ft/s^2$ or $9.8 \, m/s^2$, at the surface of Earth.

The angular accelerometer works on a similar principle, but is shaped differently so as to measure circular acceleration, such as might be given to the flywheel of an engine. The body of known mass makes the disc revolve, twisting the spring. Angular acceleration is measured in $degrees/s^2$ or $radians/s^2$ (2π radians being equivalent to $360°$).

Below: An accelerometer being installed in a dummy prior to a crash test at the Motor Industry Research Association laboratory in England.

See also: Aerodynamics; Aerospace industry; Automobile; Brake; Dynamics; Gravitation; Gyrocompass; Inertial guidance.

Achromatic lens

An achromatic lens is a combination of two lenses made of different types of glass, and has considerably less *chromatic aberration* (false color) than a single lens. All high quality lens systems in modern binoculars, cameras and other optical instruments use achromatic lenses.

A single lens refracts (bends) parallel light and focuses it to a point. The distance of this point from the lens depends upon both the curvature of the lens and the *refractive index* (light-bending power) of the lens material.

A slightly different refractive index applies to each color of light. Consequently when white light, which is a mixture of all colors, passes through a simple lens, the various colors are dispersed and are focused at different points. This produces an image with the rainbow-colored fringes characteristic of chromatic aberration.

Different types of glass have different refractive indexes, so that one type may be used to compensate for the chromatic aberration of another. It is possible to construct a compound lens (two lenses stuck together) with two types of glass of different curvatures fitted into each other; this is free from chromatic aberration for two colors of light. Crown glass and flint glass are the two most commonly used types.

When white light passes through an achromatic lens corrected for, say, red and blue, there will still be a slight chromatic aberration caused by the other colors, such as green. For high-class photographic work, lenses are made with three or more types of glass to eliminate almost all chromatic aberration for white light. These are called *apochromatic* or *process* lenses.

Before the invention of the achromatic lens, by John Dolland in 1758, it was difficult to build powerful refracting telescopes for astronomy. By using a lens with very shallow curves, chromatic aberration was reduced but at the expense of making the telescope extremely long. Some instruments of this type were made and had to be suspended from towers, making them very awkward to use. In the 17th century Sir Isaac Newton believed that it was impossible to overcome the colored fringes produced by lenses, and he invented the reflecting astronomical telescope with a mirror, which reflects all colors equally, instead of a lens.

Even with well-made modern instruments, chromatic aberration is often seen, particularly when looking through a telescope or pair of binoculars at a dark object against a bright sky. A lens which is well-corrected will show barely detectable apple green and plum red fringes. Poorly made lenses give vivid blue and orange fringes.

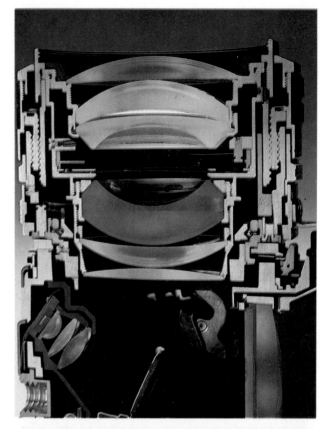

Top: Modern lenses use a number of elements, employing several types of glass with different properties to eliminate aberration.
Above: This photograph of a black-and-white grid, taken with a simple lens, shows the effect of chromatic aberration.

See also: Astronomical telescope; Binoculars; Camera; Glass; Lens; Light; Optics; Telescope.

Acid

The quality that distinguishes an acid from other substances is that its molecules contain hydrogen ATOMS which partly split away from the rest of the MOLECULE when the acid is dissolved in water. This causes the hydrogen atoms to become electrically charged IONS with a strong tendency to react with other substances – hence the corrosiveness of many acids. The molecules of strong acids have a great tendency to split.

The main acids manufactured and used in industry are sulfuric, nitric and hydrochloric acid – all of which are strong acids – and acetic acid, a relatively weak *organic* acid, that is, one with a chemical formula related to the complex carbon compounds found in living things.

Below: A sulfuric acid manufacturing plant. The complex pipework is made of steel and the acid is contained by noncorrodable linings.

Sulfuric acid

Sulfuric acid is a clear, oily liquid with the chemical formula H_2SO_4. It dominates the market for acids.

It can be manufactured directly from sulfur, or from anhydrite (calcium sulfate), a common mineral that is also used for making cement. Other sources include the sulfur-containing by-products of other industrial processes.

The original and traditional method of making sulfuric acid is by the *chamber* or *tower* process, so called because the main reaction takes place in a lead-lined chamber, and other parts of the process in towers. The acid is manufactured by burning sulfur to give sulfur dioxide and reacting this with air and steam in the presence of oxides of nitrogen, which act as CATALYSTS. The reaction is complex, on account of the presence of the catalyst, but basically it is:

$$2SO_2 \ + \ 2H_2O \ + \ O_2 \ \rightarrow \ 2H_2SO_4$$

sulfur dioxide   water   oxygen   sulfuric acid

The chamber process yields acid of a rather low strength and purity, and its use has dwindled until now only about 2 per cent of sulfuric acid is made by it. It has been supplanted by the more sophisticated *Contact* process, which gives very pure acid of any strength. It can even produce the acid in a super-charged form called *oleum* or *fuming sulfuric acid,* which has the chemical formula $H_2S_2O_7$. This intensely reactive and highly dangerous substance turns into ordinary H_2SO_4 when added to water ($H_2S_2O_7+H_2O\rightarrow 2H_2SO_4$); if, on the other hand the water is added to the acid, the reaction boils the water violently, spraying water and acid. In the Contact process, sulfur or sulfur-containing material is burned with dry air to produce sulfur dioxide (the air can be conveniently dried by using some of the acid, which readily absorbs water). The sulfur dioxide (SO_2) is filtered, then passed to a converter, where more air is added in the presence of a catalyst (platinum or vanadium pentoxide) to convert it to sulfur trioxide (SO_3).

This could now be added to water to make sulfuric acid ($SO_3+H_2O\rightarrow H_2SO_4$), but the reaction is rather violent so in practice it is added to the acid itself to make oleum ($SO_3+H_2SO_4\rightarrow H_2S_2O_7$). This can then be diluted with water.

Many stages of the process produce intense heat; this is controlled, and also used, in *waste heat boilers*. Water is pumped past the hot chemicals in a

Below: The Contact process produces very high quality acid using only sulfur, air and water.

SULFURIC ACID MANUFACTURE

Solid sulfur is tipped into the sulfur melter and melted by passing steam through it in a coil. Impurities sink to the bottom and are drained away at intervals. The molten sulfur is piped to the sulfur burner, where it is burned in air that has been dried by passing it through acid. The sulfur combines with the oxygen in the air to make sulfur dioxide. The reaction produces heat, which is used to boil water in a waste-heat boiler. The steam is used to melt more sulfur, and also to power a turbine that drives the air pump. From the boiler the sulfur dioxide is passed through a filter and then to a converter, where it is mixed with air and passed over a catalyst. This turns part of it into sulfur trioxide and generates more heat, which is used in another boiler. Next, the gas goes through a second converter, which turns it into almost pure sulfur trioxide. The last remnants of heat are extracted by a small economizer, and the gas is mixed with ready-made sulfuric acid in an absorbing tower to make oleum, a superconcentrated form. The oleum is diluted with water to the required strength, after which the acid requires cooling again before it can be piped off to the storage tanks.

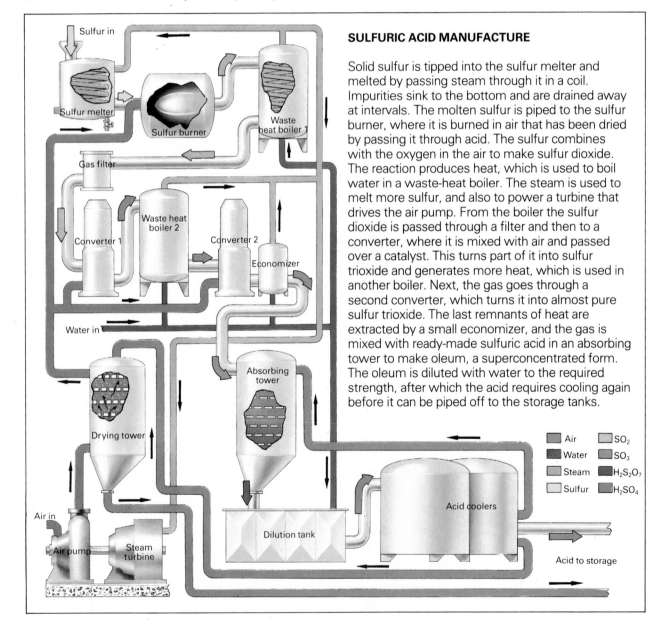

closed coil. The heat turns it to steam, which is then used in other parts of the process.

Of the sulfuric acid produced, about one-third goes to make fertilizers. Other important uses are in the production of paints, pigments, fibers, detergents and plastics.

Nitric acid

This acid has the formula HNO_3. It is a colorless, fuming liquid when in a pure state, but it is unstable and soon acquires a yellow or red color when exposed to the air. This is caused by the presence of the gas nitrogen dioxide, which forms as the acid is decomposed by light or high temperatures:

$$4HNO_3 \rightarrow 2H_2O + 4NO_2 + O_2$$
nitric acid   water   nitrogen dioxide   oxygen

Above: Sulfuric acid manufacture in nature. Villagers of El Chichon, Mexico, take cover from volcanic rain.

The fumes of nitrogen dioxide are extremely poisonous, and the acid itself is one of the most corrosive known. It cannot be stored in a bottle with a cork or rubber stopper, since it attacks both these materials. It has to be transported in stainless steel or aluminum containers.

Nitric acid is produced in the laboratory (and was once produced in industry) by treating sodium nitrate with sulfuric acid:

$$NaNO_3 + H_2SO_4 \rightarrow NaHSO_4 + HNO_3$$
sodium nitrate   sulfuric acid   sodium hydrogen sulfate   nitric acid

The modern industrial technique is to make the acid from ammonia (itself prepared by extracting nitrogen from the atmosphere), which is treated with air in the presence of a platinum-rhodium catalyst to produce nitric oxide:

$$4NH_3 + 5O_2 + 4NO \quad 6H_2O$$
ammonia   oxygen   nitric oxide   water

Further air is then admitted to the converter vessel in which the reaction takes place. This turns the nitric oxide to nitrogen dioxide:

$$2NO + O_2 \rightarrow 2NO_2$$
nitric oxide   oxygen   nitrogen dioxide

Finally, the nitrogen dioxide is dissolved in water. With the help of more atmospheric oxygen, it forms nitric acid.

$$4NO_2 + 2H_2O + O_2 \rightarrow 4HNO_3$$
nitrogen dioxide   water   oxygen   nitric acid

Nitric acid is used for making fertilizers, explosives, dyes and drugs, and also for etching, because it attacks almost all metals. A mixture of one part of nitric acid to three of hydrochloric acid, called *aqua regia*, will even dissolve gold.

Hydrochloric acid

The formula of this acid is HCl. In the pure state it is a gas, but is always used and sold as a solution in water. It is extremely corrosive in either state, and is transported in glass or rubber-lined tanks.

Hydrochloric acid is most commonly manufactured by the ELECTROLYSIS of brine (salt water). The reaction also produces caustic soda (sodium hydroxide):

$$NaCl + H_2O \rightarrow NaOH + HCl$$
salt   water   sodium hydroxide   hydrochloric acid

Hydrochloric acid is used for pickling steel before it is galvanized (zinc-plated), for decomposing bones to make gelatin, in the manufacture of dyes and rayon, refining oils, fats and waxes, tanning leather and purifying silica.

Acetic acid

This acid has a more complex structure than the other three mentioned above. Its chemical formula is conventionally written CH_3COOH, which describes its molecular structure to a certain extent as well as its content. Acetic acid is the principal ingredient of vinegar, giving it its sour taste (nearly all acids taste sour, but most are poisonous).

Uses include making cellulose acetate for synthetic fibers, plastics and packaging, vinyl acetate for emulsion paint and adhesives, acetate ester solvents for paint and plastics, synthetic fibers, and pharmaceuticals.

See also: Alkali; Amino acid; Atom and molecule; Chemical analysis; Fiber, synthetic; Ion and ionization; Salt, chemical.

Acoustics

Acoustics is the science of sound: its various branches deal with the production, transmission, reproduction and recording of sound, as well as the way it propagates and the effect enclosed spaces have upon the way we experience it.

Being a wave motion of air molecules in the atmosphere, sound obeys the rules of reflection, diffraction and dispersion in a similar fashion to the far shorter wavelength electromagnetic waves which we call light, but obviously from, and through, different materials. The wave length difference is, in fact, crucial. Sound waves are generally long enough to be diffracted quite severely by everyday objects, because their wave lengths are usually similar to the dimensions of the objects.

The wave nature of sound is particularly important in *architectural acoustics*, where the detailed design of a concert or lecture hall depends crucially on how the designers wish sound to propagate through it. Other branches of acoustics deal with the design of sound recording and reproduction systems *(engineering acoustics)* and the highly specialized field of musical instruments *(musical acoustics)*. But perhaps the most interesting, and

latest field of acoustic research is *psychoacoustics* which deals with the way we actually perceive sound. Collaboration between the engineers and the psychoacousticians has led to some very sophisticated hi-fi systems which can fool the listener – via headphones or specially designed loudspeaker arrays – that he or she is hearing sound images which are not really there.

Hi-fi systems and psychoacoustics

Hi-fi originally stood for *high fidelity,* and the primary aim of hi-fi systems was to reproduce, as faithfully as possible, the listening experience of a live performance. With the advent of purely electric instruments, such as the electric guitar and the synthesizer, the aims of the hi-fi designers changed slightly. Much modern music is recorded as a collection of separate tracks on a studio master tape – and the aim of the new generation of hi-fi equipment has been to reproduce the recorded information (which has probably never been performed live, with all the instruments playing together) as accurately as possible and as lifelike.

So today the demands put upon a music reproduction system are twofold: it must be able to recreate live music recorded in a real acoustic, conveying something of the sense of space and reverberation

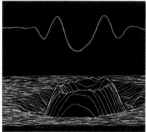

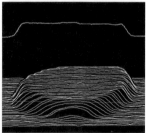

Top and above: Scan profiles showing two loudspeaker vibration patterns. The profile is built up by a scanning laser. The better speaker cone is the lower, more even, one. Left: Absorptive interior of an anechoic chamber.

Right: The acoustics of a concert hall are determined by its shape and the way sound is reflected around inside it. In this example, where length exceeds width, reflections from the walls and ceiling provide a reverberant sound field (blue), superimposed upon the direct sound (red) from the stage.

Right: Fan-shaped auditoria are most suitable for speech and directionally amplified material. The walls are lined with sound absorbing material to keep reflections to a minimum and the public address systems used in such halls are designed to beam direct sound (red) loudly right to the back of the hall. Some reflected sound (blue) is inevitable, but it is at fairly low level.

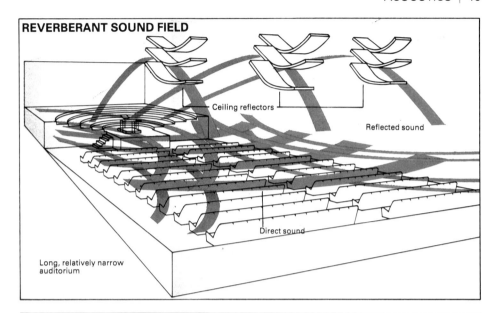

REVERBERANT SOUND FIELD

Ceiling reflectors

Reflected sound

Direct sound

Long, relatively narrow auditorium

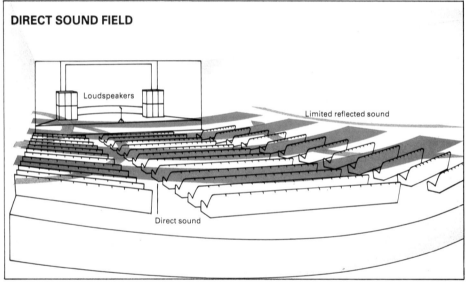

DIRECT SOUND FIELD

Loudspeakers

Limited reflected sound

Direct sound

which resonates through such performances – but it must be able to handle program sources which have been created only on tape and generally have all sorts of added reverberation and tonal doctoring.

No system can be perfect. In order to capture a live performance through a microphone or a direct electric input from, say, a synthesizer, the input signal must be processed by electronics which inevitably introduce distortion into the original signal. Indeed, the microphone and eventually the loudspeaker often add more unwanted components to the signal than the amplifier does. The original signal can be recorded on tape as a series of varying magnetized stripes in an oxide coating or, on disc, as a wavy groove in the surface plastic. Most recently, the best recordings have been produced as a series of digital pulses encoded on a special light reflecting disc, scanned by the laser of a compact disc player to recapture the original signal. Digitally encoded music, recorded direct, offers the purest signal. The electronics that decode the series of pulses, which are turned eventually into sound waves, allow none of the spurious distortion signals that are associated with other ANALOG types of recording.

Modern hi-fi systems accept a variety of input sources – tape, disc, AM RADIO, FM RADIO or digital disc. It is in the reproduction of the recorded signal that the psychoacoustician makes a significant contribution – although if material is originally recorded with multidirectional microphones to produce a set of signals that can be subsequently processed electronically the task of the hi-fi system can be made simpler.

The simplest such technique is stereophony. Original music is recorded with two microphones set at an angle to each other, so they pick up slightly

Above: Sound reflector panels on the ceiling of this conference hall help to insure that speech is clearly distributed throughout the auditorium.

different signals. If the music is electronic in origin, pseudo-stereo parallel tracks can be produced. The two signals are recorded and amplified separately and fed to two loudspeakers spaced some distance apart in the listening room. Because the PHASE of the sound waves coming from each speaker is different – the waves from one speaker are slightly out of step with those from the other – the ear is fooled into hearing a complete sound image spread between the two speakers, with different instruments and singers apparently coming from different directions; much like a 3-D image.

Further developments of this type of aural trickery have involved four or more loudspeakers and specially encoded program sources. Overall, the technique is known as *ambisonics* and its intention, like that of the original stereo systems, is to recreate the exact sound field perceived by a listener in a natural acoustic. Its exact working depends on the ability of the electronics to manipulate the phase and loudness of the sound fed to each speaker. The most sophisticated ambisonic systems can literally change the perceived acoustics of the same piece of music from a country village hall to a grand concert hall at the flick of a switch.

Architectural acoustics

In any auditorium the whole audience must be able to hear clearly the performer or musician on the stage, without undue echoes. For some types of music, notably choral and organ music, a degree of echo or reverberation actually makes the sound more pleasant, but to hear speech clearly this reverberation must be kept to a minimum. The *reverberation time* (RT) of a concert hall – the time taken for an initial burst of sound to fall to half of its original level – depends on its shape and the

materials of which it is made. Auditoria designed for large scale orchestral works are generally oblong-shaped, so there are plenty of reflections from the sides of the hall into the audience. This *reverberant field* combines with the directly radiated sound from the musicians and lends a pleasing air of *ambience* to the music. For speech, the reverberation time of a hall should be less than one second; for chamber music around one to two seconds and for full orchestras over two seconds.

Rock concerts provide a great problem for many concert halls. The sound energy is enormous and usually has artificial reverberation components added electronically. The reverberation field in some parts of conventional auditoria can easily swamp the detail in the music. The best type of hall for this sort of music is a fan-shaped arrangement, like the old movie theaters. The rock band can then concentrate their output into direct beams covering parts of the hall without much reflection from the side walls which create reverberation.

Even in conventional halls the RT can be controlled by moveable absorbers and reflectors. Some venues can even alter their acoustics by recycling the original sound through arrays of loudspeakers placed strategically throughout the auditorium.

See also: Air; Ear; Hi-Fi system; Loudspeaker; Sound; Soundproofing; Wave motion.

• FACT FILE •

- In the flying laboratories of the Space Shuttle sound waves are being used to suspend research materials without visible means of support. Acoustic levitation uses the radiation pressure of intense acoustic waves to balance out gravity so that the experimental object floats in one position.

- Acoustic detection is used to guide acoustical torpedoes onto their targets. Sounds from the engine, propeller, and other attributes of the target are picked up, or else the detector emits sonar pulses. Once in the target area, the detector controls the torpedo servomechanisms.

- Nondestructive testing, which employs high-frequency sound waves along with powerful microcomputers, helps engineers to monitor invisible pipe-line welds, the condition of pressure vessels inside nuclear reactors, and hidden faults deep inside metal components.

Adhesive

Until this century, the only adhesives available were derived from natural sources such as bones and plant saps. With the development of synthetic polymers, however, an enormous diversity of new adhesives became available. Today, adhesives range from the gum on postage stamps to the epoxy resins used in aircraft and bridge building.

Science and industry have developed many types of adhesives for various uses, but the basic mechanism of adhesion is still not well understood. At one time it was thought to involve a mechanical

Left: Epoxy adhesive grout was used to bond these precast concrete sections of a bridge in Northern England.
Top: Contact adhesives will only set in the absence of air. The bond is immediate on contact of the surfaces and hardens rapidly.
Above: Sealing compound oozes from the join of an auto engine block and head. The compound insures complete contact between the sides of the gasket and the surface of the head and block.

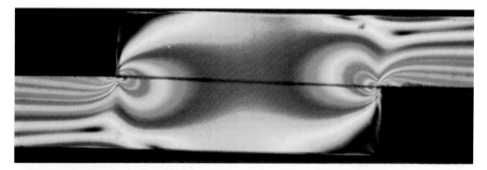

Left: Polarized light shining through two clear plastic sheets shows clearly the stress concentrations around an adhesive bond. Below left: Brake linings are glued with complex phenolic resins. Above right: The molecular life of a superglue from tube to fully hardened adhesive. (1) Acidic stabilizer (red) stops adhesive molecules (white) from linking and keeps adhesive in liquid state. (2) Water (blue) on surfaces to be joined neutralizes stabilizer. (3) Adhesive molecules join and curing begins. (4) Adhesive molecules build up on surfaces and interweave.

attachment: liquid adhesive flowed into pores or cavities in the *adherends* (the materials being stuck), hardened into a solid and thus locked them together.

This is now thought to contribute something to the strength of the bond, but not considered to be its main cause.

The current belief is that adhesion is caused by chemical and physical forces of the same kind as those that hold the atoms and molecules of the adherends themselves together. But exactly how these forces are called into play still is not known.

The adhesive must normally be applied to both surfaces that are to be joined together, because no matter how smooth they seem they will be full of irregularities at a molecular level which must be evened out if the process is to be successful.

Design of joints

An adhesive joint of the normal type has five parts, which may be considered as five links in a chain – the joint being as strong as the weakest link. They are: the inherent strength (or *cohesion*) of one material, the strength of the bond of the adhesive to

it, the inherent strength of the adhesive itself, the strength of its bond to the other material, and the strength of the other material.

With most types of adhesive, the strength of the bond between adhesive and adherend is stronger than the cohesion of the adhesive itself. For this reason, it is important to keep the adhesive film as thin as possible to prevent the joint from failing.

The joining surfaces of the adherends must therefore fit together exactly. They must also have a large enough area, and the right shape, so as not to overstress the joint. Adhesive joints resist shear (sideways forces) and tension as well, but do not stand up to peeling forces, where there is tension at one edge of the joint that can cause a split to form and spread.

More and more joints in manufactured goods of all types are being made with adhesives instead of more traditional methods such as bolting or welding. This even includes metal to metal joints: recent examples include aluminum chair leg assemblies and certain parts of aircraft, where honeycomb structures of light alloy are bonded between two aluminum panels.

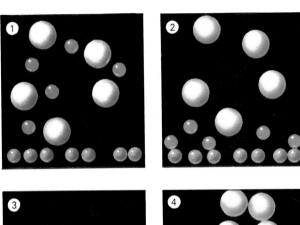

In joints of this type, the adhesive cannot normally be used as direct replacement for the earlier fastening method, and the joint has to be redesigned from scratch. Sometimes the adhesive is used as a supplement to a mechanical fastening: parts are spot-welded together and the space between the welds filled with adhesive to steady the parts against vibration.

It is important to choose the right adhesive for a

Below: An exploded view of the Fokker F28 showing the use of adhesives in its construction. Over 20 years of operational service there has been no known case of bonded joint failure in this aircraft.

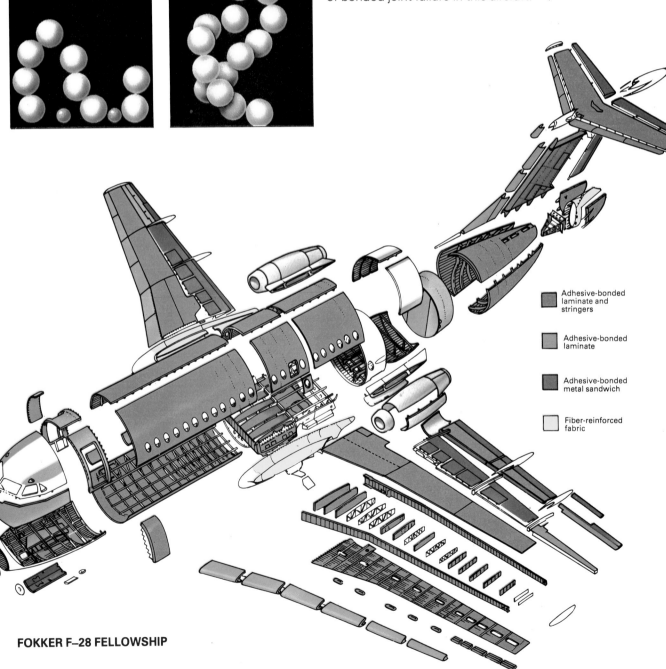

Adhesive-bonded laminate and stringers

Adhesive-bonded laminate

Adhesive-bonded metal sandwich

Fiber-reinforced fabric

FOKKER F–28 FELLOWSHIP

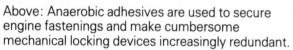

Above: Anaerobic adhesives are used to secure engine fastenings and make cumbersome mechanical locking devices increasingly redundant.

Above: Cutaway of a bearing retainer and threadlock sealed with an anaerobic adhesive, which hardens in the presence of metal and absence of air.

job. For example, joints between flexible materials must be made with a flexible adhesive. In industry, other factors are also important, for example, setting time. It is no use cutting manufacturing costs by using adhesive joints instead of more expensive fastenings if the whole industrial process is held up while everyone waits for the adhesive to set.

Types of adhesive

Natural adhesives may come from animal, vegetable or mineral sources. They may be *hot-melt* adhesives, which come in solid form, melt on heating and harden on cooling. They may be *water-soluble*: adhesives of this type may be in the form of liquids or powders which dissolve in water; either kind remains soluble even after it has dried, so they are not water resistant. The adhesive may also be dissolved in an *organic solvent* which evaporates faster than water, thus allowing it to set quickly. This type of adhesive is normally water resistant.

The name glue is widely used for any type of adhesive, but strictly speaking only applies to protein derivatives, that is, gelatinlike adhesives made from animal or vegetable protein. Scotch glue and similar types of woodworking glue are made by the traditional method of boiling down bones. They are hot-melt adhesives. A newer type, soyabean glue, is made of vegetable protein. Casein glue is a water-soluble woodworking adhesive made from milk.

Natural starches, cellulose and gums from various plants are used to make light, inexpensive water-soluble adhesives. These are much used in the paper industry, and also in the home as wallpaper paste and office paste and gum. The adhesive on stamps and envelopes is gum arabic.

Natural rubber, generally dissolved in air-drying organic solvents, makes adhesives that are used in industry for glueing rubber and leather, in building for attaching wall and floor coverings, and in drawing offices for glueing paper (because it does not make the paper wrinkle and can easily be removed without leaving a mark).

Natural resins and bitumens include black top, which is used to bind aggregate (gravel) in road making and similar applications. Marine glue is a natural resin in an organic solvent. It is not a true glue; true glues are not water resistant enough for marine use. Sealing wax is a hot-melt natural resin.

All the previously mentioned adhesives are organic in origin. There is one inorganic natural adhesive: *water-glass* (sodium silicate) which is used in the paper industry.

Most modern proprietary adhesives are based on synthetic rubber/resin formulations. Synthetic adhesives are generally called synthetic resins because the natural adhesives they most resemble are the resin types. There are many variations, including one not found in natural adhesives: the

Left: Leaping from wave to wave at speeds of up 100 mph (160km/h) powerboats demonstrate the versatility of modern adhesives. Using the whole range of glues, such varied tasks as holding the laminated hull together and proofing the electrics are tackled with ease.

Above: Smoothing away excess resin along the join between sections of a glass fiber auto body. Epoxy resins retain their adhesion and are waterproof.

two-part adhesive, where the adhesive is mixed with a separate *hardener* or *catalyst* to make it set. Synthetic resins are normally classed as *thermoplastic* (melting when heated) and *thermosetting* (heat speeds hardening).

Thermoplastic adhesives include the *vinyl resins,* a versatile group that stick well to glass and metal, but are aso used in many other applications. Polyvinyl acetate (PVA) based adhesive is water-soluble and used for woodwork, ceramic tiling, flooring and general purpose bonding agents.

Other types of adhesive have organic solvents or are hot-melt types, such as the resin that is sandwiched between two thin layers of glass to make laminated safety glass for automobile windshields, making them stronger and safer.

Acrylic resins

There are several types of *acrylic resin* adhesives, one- and two-part, both cured by adding chemicals. They can develop very strong bonds, and are more transparent than other types of adhesive. Objects are often embedded in clear acrylic resin for protection or display. One unusual type is *cyanoacrylate* adhesive, the popular Superglue that cures to a high strength in a few seconds. This quality makes it useful for production lines.

Cellulose adhesives consist of chemicals derived from cellulose (such as cellulose acetate) in an air drying organic solvent, and are not the same as the water-based natural cellulose pastes mentioned above. They are quick drying and water resistant.

Other thermosetting resins include the *phenolics*, which are available both as chemical solvent types and in thin, solid, pressure-sensitive sheets which are used by the plywood industry for glueing layers of wood together.

Thermosetting adhesives include *epoxide resins*, among the strongest of all adhesives. Some types will withstand a shearing stress of up to 7000 lb/sq in. (500 kg/cm^2) in correctly designed joints.

Polyester resins are cheaper than epoxy resins, and are therefore suitable for use in bulk. Their commonest use is with glass fiber to make glass reinforced plastics.

Synthetic rubber is used with organic solvents and with water to make many types of adhesives. The pressure-sensitive adhesives which are used on adhesive tape can also be of this type. Synthetic rubber adhesives are widely used in automobiles for attaching interior trim panels.

Two products that do not fit into any of these categories, but which are nonetheless adhesives, are solder and hydraulic cement.

See also: Bitumen; Bond, chemical; Catalyst; Glass fiber; Plastics; Polymer and polymerization; Rubber, natural; Rubber, synthetic.

Sticking people together

On Vietnam's battlefields, doctors were faced with massive numbers of casualties – many with horrifyingly severe internal wounds and in imminent danger of bleeding to death. The task of the surgeon was to treat each casualty effectively but quickly in order to move on to the next patient. A new kind of wound dressing was needed to speed up the surgical procedures accordingly. Tissue adhesive or surgical glue, applied by spraying, proved highly valuable in dealing with serious hemorrhaging under pressure of time.

The idea of a quick-acting tissue adhesive has been a surgeon's dream for many years. For instance, when operating to repair the liver of a soldier wounded by shrapnel, massive bleeding must be brought under control within minutes – but the delicate tissue of the liver requires painstaking stitching that demands hours of concentrated work. A quicker answer lies in a spray can.

Ideally, the surgeon would be able to spray the bleeding regions with a fine transparent film, which bonds immediately with the tissue, creating a complete seal and staunching the flow of blood. Then the surgeon could hold together the edges of the cut tissue and rejoin them with a swift spray from the same can. When the patient wakes up and surveys his stomach, all he would see is a thin line marking the length of the first incision: no stitches no clips, no staples.

Sadly, this ideal procedure is not yet a reality. The enticing idea that wounds – from superficial grazes to internal hemorrhages – might be safely sealed by the simple application of an appropriate glue has attracted the research departments of several major drug companies for at least 20 years. The fruits of that research have been marketed and they show great promise in a number of specialized applications. A satisfactory product for general surgery is still, however, only a dream.

Surgical glues so far developed are based around a family of compounds known as cyanoacrylates. These are organic compounds that are compatible with the biochemistry of living systems, and that are more or less nontoxic to living cells. In the presence of moisture, these compounds undergo a rapid reaction as strong chemical bonds are formed between individual cyanoacrylate molecules. This reaction – called polymerization – changes the compound from a liquid into a semi-solid gel with considerable strength. Extra bonds

are also formed between individual cyanoacrylate molecules and the surrounding tissue. The result is a tough lattice of molecular chains firmly fixed at the site of application.

One of the most severe problems with tissue adhesives is an inflammation of the wound caused by a slightly toxic reaction to the glue. Following the original injury, this irritation increases the chances of post-operative infection at the site of the wound. Both local healing and overall recovery are often slowed. Furthermore, the medical teams using surgical glue in Vietnam found evidence that even noninflamed wounds sealed with the adhesive did not heal as fast as those closed with conventional stitches. Possibly, this retardation of the healing process may be due to the adhesive film slowing the penetration of new cells across the gap and preventing microscopic blood capillaries from growing back into the wounded region.

Since Vietnam, research into surgical glue has

Above: High-speed surgical techniques are needed to deal with the high casualty rates produced on modern battlefields.

discovered one solution to both these problems: use less adhesive. A recurring problem with the battlefield trials will be familiar to anyone who has ever used spray paint. The spray nozzles kept getting blocked. To avoid this, the spray cans used in Vietnam tended to have large holes — but this meant that it was difficult for the surgeons to apply the adhesive in minimum amounts. Today, special aerosol designs can eliminate the problem of blocking and so it is possible to apply the adhesive in very thin layers. Transparent flexible shields are also used to confine the spray to just the areas required.

There are three broad surgical applications where existing tissue adhesives have won a firm place. The first is where bonds are required in tissues which are so delicate that conventional stitching is either impossible or extremely time consuming. Brain surgery is one example where it is impossible to stitch thread in an organ which has a consistency (when alive) like soft peanut butter. Surgical glue, usually applied as drops rather than as a spray, is often used toward the end of a brain operation to seal regions that have become exposed or weakened by the surgeon's scalpel.

Another area where surgical glue has already found a place is in combination with conventional stitching. This approach is now common in plastic surgery where tissue adhesive, usually applied as a spray, can leave much less of a scar than stitches.

Thread and glue can be used sequentially as well as simultaneously. Stitches are used at first where a strong bond is required. Then, just as soon as the wound has sealed, the stitches are taken out and the tissue is held in place with a light film of surgical glue. The final stages of healing can thus take place with no danger of stitch marks being left.

The third established use for surgical glue harks back to its battlefield trials in Vietnam: it is valuable in catastrophies and disasters where time is critical and where long-term disadvantages must take a back seat to the immediate priority of saving lives. Paramedics and emergency medical teams tending the victims of air crashes and earthquakes are increasingly being trained in the use of adhesive sprays. A derivative is also being used with great success to treat burns where it is important to halt fluid loss and to seal out infection.

Although these specialized applications are all important, surgical glue is today used in less than one per cent of operations. Partly, this is because surgeons are a cautious group and any innovation takes time to be accepted. But also, doctors are waiting for the drug companies to market a new generation of tissue adhesives which are free from the present limitations.

The most important breakthrough will come with the successful development of a surgical glue which is entirely nontoxic and which can be broken down by the body and absorbed into the bloodstream once the wound has healed. Certain compounds, particularly those based around ordinary gelatin, look promising. But remaining difficulties include insufficient bond strength and problems of applying the gelatin glue as a spray.

With an enormous market ready and waiting, sooner or later the drug companies will come up with a satisfactory surgical glue for general use. Then the needle and thread can be put away and surgery should become faster and safer, saving more lives and leaving fewer scars.

Aerial photography

Aerial photography – taking photographs of the surface of the Earth from the air – has many important civil uses such as mapping and crop surveying, as well as its military applications which include spying and battlefield reconnaissance.

There are two basic techniques involved in aerial photography, called *oblique* and *vertical*. Oblique photography is the simpler – it just involves flying over the site in a small plane while a photographer on board takes pictures using a hand held camera through an open window, the line of sight being at an angle to the ground. Such pictures are used mainly for their pictorial value, or for illustrating various types of land forms.

Vertical photography is a much more exacting technique, and uses large custom-built cameras mounted in the floor of the aircraft. As the term suggests, the cameras look vertically downward.

A typical camera has a high-quality lens of 150 mm focal length, carefully designed so as not to introduce distortions into the image. The camera uses a 250 ft (76 m) roll of film 9 in. (230 mm) wide, and has a suction back to pull the film flat while the pictures are being taken. Exposure times vary from 1/200 to 1/1000 sec, depending on light conditions and the movement of the image being photographed.

The heights used for aerial surveys vary with local conditions and requirements, but are usually well above 1300 ft (400 m). The rate at which photo-

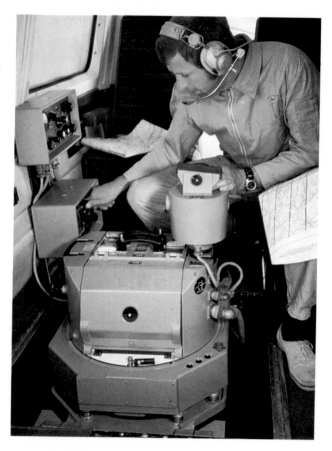

Above: A large, custom-built aerial photography camera. This type is fixed to the floor of the aircraft and is used for vertical photography.
Below left: The once mysterious River Amazon and its surrounding tropical forest, once impervious to the advance of civilization, now charted and opened up for development by aerial surveying.

graphs are taken varies with the image speed, since the aim is to make each shot overlap the former by 60 per cent. In this way, stereoscopic views are taken. Picture taking rates vary from a few seconds to one taken every couple of minutes.

Survey photographs are normally taken in black and white, on panchromatic film. But in recent years other types of film have been used, notably those sensitive to the INFRARED wavelengths. Infrared radiation penetrates haze much better than visible light, which makes photographs taken from high altitude much clearer. In addition, the amount of infrared radiation emitted by an object changes with its temperature. This makes it possible, when using a scanning image, to distinguish between warm and cold water, for example, so that the discharges from factories into rivers can be monitored to make sure they are not overheating the water. The amount of heat absorbed from the Sun by living and dead vegetation is different, so the state of a

Above: An infrared picture of the San Fransisco Bay area and the Golden Gate Bridge taken from an aircraft flying at a height of 60,000 ft (18,000 m).

field or forest can easily be seen at a glance.

Infrared pictures cannot be printed in infrared, so false-color film is generally used. This renders infrared as red, red as green and green as blue. It is insensitive to blue light. Another device, the *air-scan thermograph*, uses an electronic scanner similar to a television camera to record infrared radiation only, ignoring visible colors altogether.

More detailed information can be obtained with the *multiband* camera, a device which takes nine simultaneous pictures of the same scene. It is loaded with nine combinations of film and color filters.

Pictures can also be taken with side-looking airborne radar (slar for short) which has the advantage that it works in complete darkness or fog. This makes it particularly suitable for military use. Unfortunately, the quality of the picture is not very good, though it is steadily being improved.

Photographs have been taken from the air almost since the beginnings of photography itself. The first aerial photograph known was taken from the basket of a balloon over France in 1856. By the 1880s, photographs were being taken from balloons, kites and even rockets in the course of experiments in Europe, and in 1909 from aircraft, both in France and America.

The French were early pioneers in both aviation and photography. At the outbreak of World War I they already had some aerial photographs taken in peacetime of the very places the German Army was invading.

The French photographs provided the inspiration for better aerial photography. J. T. C. Moore Brabazon (later Lord Brabazon), a keen photographer in charge of the British Army's air reconnaissance team, experimented with old-fashioned bellows cameras but found them useless. They could not be kept still in the slipstream of an aircraft flying at 80 mph (130 km/h). So he designed a camera suitable for inserting in the floor of an airplane – the first purpose-built aerial camera.

By the end of the war, these had developed into huge devices with focal lengths as great as 6 ft (1.83 m) to give fine detail.

Moore-Brabazon also introduced the use of a stereoscope to view pairs of pictures taken from slightly different points, giving an exaggeratedly three-dimensional effect that allowed the heights of objects taken from above to be measured.

From spying to mapping

At the end of World War I, the newly developed techniques of aerial photography were applied to peaceful uses – though a certain amount of spying still continued. The main applications were map making and surveying, but there were other uses.

In Canada, forests being grown for timber were photographed from the air as early as 1921. This was an ideal way of checking on trees.

Another use of aerial photography was discovered in the U.S. in the 1920s and 1930s. The Agricultural Production and Marketing Board regularly photographed farms from the air to check what crops were being grown. In this way, they were able not only to compile statistics, but also to detect false claims made by farmers for the subsidies that were paid for growing certain crops. This unusual peacetime spying made them extremely unpopular.

By 1938, it had become obvious to everyone that Germany was preparing for war. In Britain, the Royal Air Force commissioned the brilliant Australian aerial photographer Sidney Cotton to get as many pictures of military installations as he could without attracting attention.

Cotton had been taking aerial photographs since the early 1920s. His method of tackling the job was most ingenious. First of all, he used RAF funds to buy a Lockheed Electra, a fast civil airplane.

He modified this by installing three cameras under the floor; they were hidden by a close-fitting sliding panel when not in use. He also arranged for a stream of warm air to be blown into the camera compartment inside the airplane. The ventilation prevented the camera from fogging up or freezing at high altitudes and low temperatures, a problem

LANDSAT D SATELLITE

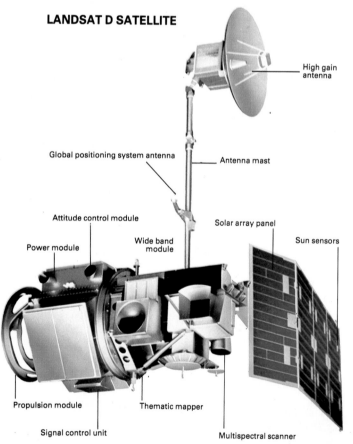

High gain antenna

Global positioning system antenna

Antenna mast

Attitude control module

Solar array panel

Power module

Wide band module

Sun sensors

Propulsion module

Thematic mapper

Signal control unit

Multispectral scanner

Above: Aerial reconnaissance in World War II. These pictures show the German rocket research station at Peenemünde before and after the RAF bombed it – such evidence formed an important part of the strategic planning during wartime.

Left: On each orbit of 35 minutes, Landsat D traces a path 115 miles (185 km) wide over the Earth's surface. It carries a wide band communications system using NASA Tracking and Data Relay satellites (TDRS) and ground-based stations.

Above: The North-South circular orbit of Landsat 3. Earth rotates 100 miles (160 km) each day, giving a complete picture of the planet in 18 days.

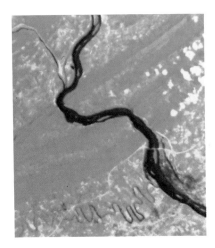

Above: Landsat image of a forest area near Harrisburg, Pennsylvania in 1976 taken to show the extent of defoliation by gypsy moths.

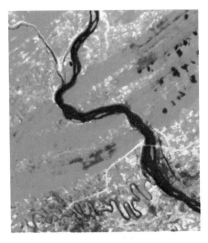

Above: The same area photographed one year later, the brown (defoliated) areas having increased in size, proving the spread of the moths.

that had dogged aerial photographers for years.

Regular aerial photography proved vital during World War II, when Sidney Cotton was given the job of organizing and running the first British photographic reconnaissance unit. Frequent pictures enabled a reference file on a place to be built up, so that troop movements, new buildings and unusual events could all be observed. One early success of the unit was the detection of the V1 and V2 sites. Subsequent bombing of the sites forced the Germans to use smaller, movable installations.

Pictures from space

Since the war, the rapid growth in space technology has led to enormous advances in vertical photography and mapping using high-resolution equipment in satellites.

By 1984 no less than seven meteorological satellites encircled the Earth at an altitude of 22,000 miles (35,000 km). Their orbits were synchronized with that of the Earth, so that they appeared to hover motionless over their allotted sectors of the planet, beaming down meteorological information as part of a joint World Weather Watch system.

In June 1978 the U.S. launched Seasat, equipped with the experimental Synthetic Aperture Radar (SAR) system that photographed the surface of the oceans by means of microwaves instead of light. Seasat's electric system malfunctioned after 100 days, but in that time produced images of extremely high quality from an altitude of 500 miles (800 km).

During the nineteenth century, only 35 per cent of the Earth's land surface has been properly mapped using photomapping techniques. The ATLAS project of the European Space Agency aims to complete a worldwide coverage of 1:50,000 scale maps pro-

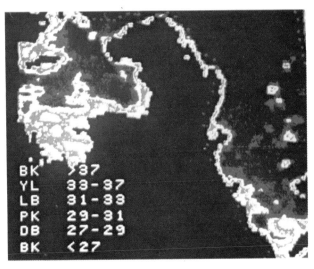

Above: Satellite image showing temperature trends relating to a freeze which hit the Florida fruit industry. Such data can be used to warn farmers of imminent frosts in advance, allowing damage to be avoided.

duced by means of a series of overlapping pictures which can be processed through photogrammetric stereoscopic devices. The high-resolution pictures are taken with a Zeiss Metric Camera mounted in the Spacelab module.

With the advent of the re-usable space shuttle, these applications have become cheaper and easier to maintain, and are already taking over many of the tasks previously carried out by conventional high-altitude aircraft.

See also: Aircraft; Camera; Film; Lens; Photographic processing; Space photography.

Aerodynamics

Aerodynamics (like hydrodynamics) is a branch of fluid dynamics, which is the study of fluids in motion. The fundamental laws governing the movements of gases, such as air, and liquids, such as water, are identical.

The equations representing these natural laws are, however, so complex that, although formulated more than 100 years ago they cannot be easily solved to account for all systems and conditions.

Even today, it takes the most powerful computers to solve the complex equations which govern the flow of fluids around irregularly shaped objects. It is a sobering thought to realize that we may be able to design craft which can enter space and glide back to Earth, but the detailed description of the way a river erodes its banks and changes course still relies a great deal on experiment rather than calculation.

Aerodynamics is of crucial importance in the design of jet engines, the turbines which drive electricity generators and even the family automobile. Reducing aerodynamic drag on anything that moves through the atmosphere, be it a car, an airplane, or a train, means greater efficiency and less fuel consumption. The study of aerodynamics in the modern world has received a huge boost from the need to conserve energy.

Air is by no means as insubstantial as it might at first appear. At sea level on a mild day the density of air is about 14.7 psi (1.23 kg/m^2). This means that a large sedan car with a cross section of about 70.6 ft^3 (2 m^3) moving at 30 mph (50 km/h) must shift about 66 lbs (30 kg) of air every second. Good aerodynamic design helps the air flow over and around the car in a smooth controlled sweep, minimizing the distance each molecule of air must be moved, and thus minimizing drag forces.

Think of the vast area of the wing surface of a jumbo jet and the high speeds at which it travels through the air, and it is not difficult to see what keeps it aloft although many other effects contribute lift as well.

The equations which describe in a general fashion the motion of fluids were first developed by C. L. M. H. Navier in 1820 and subsequently perfected by G. G. Stokes in 1845. These equations, now called the Navier-Stokes equations, relate velocity, density, pressure, compressibility, viscosity and the spatial dimensions of the fluid. Because of the number of variables involved, the subject of fluid dynamics has been broken down into a number of subdivisions where certain conditions predominate and others can be ignored. This results in a whole series of solutions – each applying in a limited range of circumstances.

Historically, hydrodynamics came first and con-

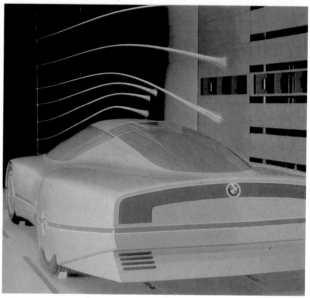

sequently includes the greater number of assumptions. Water is, however, almost incompressible, which means that the density of water does not change with the pressure applied to it. This property of water and other liquids simplifies the original Navier-Stokes equations.

Aerodynamics

At the beginning of the present century, aerodynamics began to attract more attention than hydrodynamics with the possibility of flight in air. Because of the concentration of effort, aerodynamics – building upon the theories of hydrodynamics – soon outstripped its parent. It started with the same assumptions as hydrodynamics but with the assumption of incompressibility replacing what was a fact for water. Prandtl showed that the effect of VISCOSITY for flow around streamlined (smooth) bodies was confined to a thin layer immediately adjacent to the body. This region is called the *boundary layer*. Outside the boundary layer, viscous

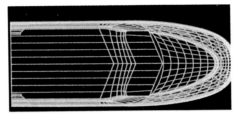
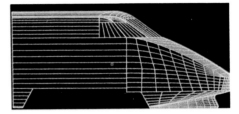

Top left: The highly streamlined shape of the French Train à Grande Vitesse (TGV) is the result of many years extensive research, using computer-generated graphics as well as wind tunnels (top right, and center). This work insures that the structure is not only strong enough to withstand the forces generated by high-speed travel, but also reduces aerodynamic drag to a minimum.

Below left: A BMW automobile body undergoes trials in the manufacturer's wind tunnel. It is through such testing at all stages of the design process that the necessary aerodynamic improvements can be incorporated in the final production model.

Right: Turbulent airflow over an airplane wing reduced by the incorporation of a laminar flow control system, whereby some of the airflow close to the surface which would other wise become turbulent on contact, can be drawn off via holes to improve aerodynamic performance and thus save fuel.

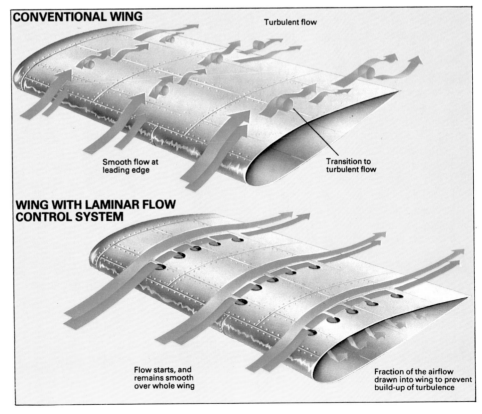

CONVENTIONAL WING

Turbulent flow

Smooth flow at leading edge

Transition to turbulent flow

WING WITH LAMINAR FLOW CONTROL SYSTEM

Flow starts, and remains smooth over whole wing

Fraction of the airflow drawn into wing to prevent build-up of turbulence

Above: Photograph taken at less than a millionth of a second showing the effect of supersonic airflow.
Right: Smoke introduced into the wind tunnel shows the formation of turbulence on a fuselage.

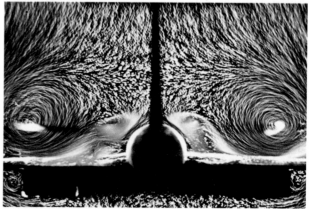

forces are negligible and consequently *potential flow* theories apply. The analysis of streamlined bodies enabled airfoil design to advance rapidly.

Whereas smooth, streamlined bodies have an unbroken and stable boundary layer, bluff (unstreamlined) bodies do not. The flow starts to separate because of misbehavior of the boundary layer and potential flow solutions, even away from the body, become inaccurate. Even today, no complete theory for low-speed flow around bluff bodies exists, but an understanding of what happens physically has been built up over the years. As aircraft speeds increased, it was found that the assumption of incompressibility introduced errors. The reason for this phenomenon can be explained by Bernoulli's equation.

Bernoulli's equation is a statement of energy conservation in a fluid. A fluid, like any moving body, has KINETIC ENERGY through its motion and potential energy because of its potential to move under the influence of the Earth's GRAVITATION. At all points in a fluid there is a static pressure proportional to the height of fluid above that point – this is a measure of the potential energy of the fluid at that point. The kinetic energy of the fluid is proportional to the square of the velocity and gives rise to a dynamic pressure. If no energy is added to or taken away from the fluid stream then total energy will be conserved even if there is an interchange between kinetic energy (dynamic pressure) and potential energy

(static pressure) – this is the principle behind Bernoulli's equation.

Because dynamic pressure is proportional to the square of the fluid velocity, the rate at which pressure changes with increasing velocity will depend on the absolute velocity as well as its rate of change. Consequently, the higher the speeds involved, the larger will be the pressure changes and the greater the density changes because of compressibility. Below 126 mph (210 km/h) the density changes can be ignored and air can be treated as incompressible, but above this airspeed the assumption becomes increasingly inaccurate.

Mach numbers and the speed of sound

Sound is a pressure wave of *small* magnitude and its speed of propagation in the fluid is called the speed of sound. The airflow around a body creates higher air pressures in the vicinity which travel upstream, giving advance warning of the presence of the body.

Familiar objects redesigned through the application of aerodynamic techniques. Top left: Streamlined racing helmet smooths airflow past a skier's head.
Top right: Revolutionary all-purpose fighter aircraft prototype (HiMAT). Above: New-look, low-slung, all-enclosed high-speed racing bike.

Because of this pressure wave the air moves in a curved path ahead of the body, passing around it with the minimum of disturbance.

If the airspeed is greater than the speed of sound, these warning signals cannot propagate upstream at all and no warning is given – this is called *supersonic flow*. In this situation the air must change direction suddenly when it encounters the body. If the deviation asked of it is small it does so, producing a small-amplitude shock wave attached to the body. If the deviation is large, a large-amplitude shock wave can move ahead of the body (large amplitude waves travel faster) and behind this the air is slowed to subsonic speed. These shock waves are commonly called sonic booms.

With such different flow systems on either side of the speed of sound, it becomes imperative to know whether the airspeed is above or below this value. Unfortunately, the speed of sound does not have a unique value, but varies with temperature. In this situation it becomes convenient to divide the airspeed by the speed of sound – this ratio is named the Mach number for Ernest Mach, an Austrian scientist who studied the flight of bullets.

Hypersonic flow

When airspeeds increase still further, the rise in temperature and pressure behind shock waves becomes so large that the air dissociates, that is, some of the molecules of nitrogen and oxygen which constitute air break down into atoms. Behind the body, temperatures and pressures decrease and the molecules re-form. This is hypersonic flow.

Slip flow

Atmospheric pressure at sea level is caused by the weight of air above the point of measurement. Consequently, at higher altitudes pressure and density decrease. There comes a height – over 50 miles (80 km) above sea level – where the density is so low that the *mean free path* (the average distance between collisions of the molecules) is the same order of magnitude as the body under consideration. Air no longer behaves as an entity (usually called a *continuum*) and pressure and forces become the result of individual molecular collisions with the body surface. This part of the subject is called *free molecular* or *Newtonian flow*. There is no sharp division between continuum and molecular flow, rather a progressive change, and this part of the subject is called *slip flow*.

See also: Air; Aircraft; Ballistics; Dynamics; Gravitation; Physics; Potential; Pressure; Space shuttle; Supersonic flight; Wind tunnel.

Aero engine

The term aero engine can, strictly speaking, be applied to any aircraft power unit, but it is normally applied to the specialized piston engines used in airplanes until they were largely succeeded by the JET engine.

The history of the development of the aero engine has been a struggle to combine high power, lightness and reliability. These qualities were also required in the automobile engine, which was developed at much the same time. But even the earliest aircraft demanded more power than the early automobile industry could produce.

When the Wright brothers came to search for an engine to put into their latest glider in 1903 they thought they could manage to fly with one of only 8 hp, provided it was not too heavy. They approached, without success, half a dozen makers of car engines. Eventually, they built their own engine and got 12 hp from it, but it was still relatively heavy at 15 lb (7 kg) to the horsepower. Thirty years later, engine designers were aiming at a power to weight ratio of over 1 hp/lb (2 hp/kg).

The Wrights' first engine had four cylinders set in line like those of a small car engine. The year after their first flight, a five-cylinder motor designed by American engineer Charles Manly developed 50 hp at a ratio of 4 lb (1.8 kg) to the horsepower.

In the years leading up to World War I, the French led the field in aero design, producing several 50 hp and two 100 hp engines by 1908. But the best of these still only had a power to weight ratio of 3.7 lb (1.7 kg) to the hp.

Early engines were water cooled, with the cylinders arranged in line or in a V-formation as in an automobile. But in 1907 a new and highly successful type was introduced; the *rotary* engine. In this, the crankcase and cylinders revolved in one piece around a stationary crankshaft. The pistons were connected to a single pivot mounted off-center, so that they moved in and out as they revolved with their cylinders. The AIRSCREW was connected directly to the front of the crankcase and turned with it.

This odd-sounding arrangement worked surprisingly well. It had fewer parts than a conventional engine, and since the cylinders moved rapidly around, they could be air cooled by fins mounted so as to take advantage of the draft. Both factors contributed to the lightness of the engine.

Rotary engines always had an odd number of cylinders. This reduced vibration, since there were never two pistons moving in exactly the same direction at the same time. The original 1907 Gnome engine had seven, and later types nine.

Other types of engine produced at the time included the Spanish Hispano-Suiza, a design well

Above: The Wright brothers built their original engine of 1903 themselves. It was a simple four-cylinder design similar to an auto engine, but much lighter. Even so, it weighed some 180 lb (80 kg) and produced a maximum of 12 hp, which was a rather poor power-to-weight ratio even in those days.

ahead of its time with eight steel cylinders arranged in a V and screwed into an aluminum block. In the later years of the war this engine yielded, in successive versions, 150, 220 and 300 hp. The Rolls-Royce Eagle, a V12 engine with a broadly similar layout adapted from an original Mercedes design, produced 360 hp in its Mark 8 version. This was the engine of the Vickers Vimy that carried Britons Alcock and Brown across the Atlantic in 1919.

The radial engine

Both the Rolls and Hispano engines had conventional water cooling. This often gave trouble, since vibration and the shock of landing caused the plumbing to break. It was to overcome this problem that a third type of engine was introduced: the air cooled *radial* engine, in which static cylinders were arranged in a circle and cooled by the backwash of the propeller.

This was not a completely new idea, since the water cooled Manly-Balzer engine of 1902, fitted to the unsuccessful Langley Aerodrome, had also been a radial. The air cooled Anzani engine that powered Blériot's cross-Channel flight of 1909 was also a kind of half-radial, with three cylinders set in a fan shape. The first of the new generation of radials was the 14-cylinder Jaguar engine made by the RAF factory at Farnborough in England in 1918.

Problems with cooling

Proper cooling is one of the most critical points of aero engine design. Aero engines have always produced far more power for their size than automobile engines of the same date, and have consequently run at much higher temperatures.

These problems led to great rivalry between the designers of air and water cooled engines. Their

Above: Pratt & Whitney's PW2037 turbofan is probably the most fuel efficient of its type in the world. It is a truly massive machine, its size and complexity belying its frugal thirst for aviation fuel, which is some 30 per cent lower than the consumption of the first generation of turbofans.

Right: Ultimate piston-power. This Wright TC18 (Turbo Compound) R3350EA Series engine, as fitted in the DC7, produced 3400 hp at takeoff for a dry weight of 3645 lb (1653 kg). Some are still in service. The impeller of the two speed gear driven supercharger can be seen at the rear.

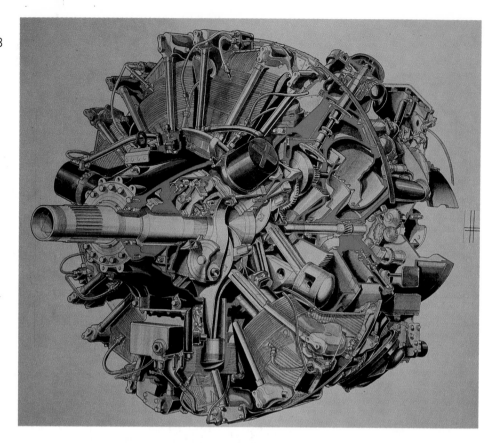

object was to produce completely reliable engines that were adequately cooled with the lightest possible system – thus improving the vital power-to-weight ratio.

As far as reliability went, the water-cooled engine seemed to have all the advantages. Any desired temperature could be maintained by altering the size of radiator fitted to the engine.

The temperature of the engine was kept within safe limits by the boiling point of the cooling water, since it could rise no higher than this until the water boiled away completely. Some engines used this feature in *evaporative* cooling systems, where the water was allowed to boil at the engine. The steam was ducted off, recondensed into water and returned to the engine. The system had been used as early as 1907 in the French Antoinette engine.

In other engines, ethylene glycol (antifreeze) was used as a coolant, raising the boiling point to 285° F (140° C) to provide an additional safety margin.

The principal trouble with this type of engine was the weight and complexity of the cooling system – it was one more thing to go wrong. Air-cooled engines did not suffer from this problem, since their system had no moving parts.

The cylinders were always arranged radially in one or more circular rows. This placed them just behind the propeller, an ideal position for cooling. They were also spaced quite wide apart, so that the

outside could be covered with large fins to increase the surface area and thus improve heat dissipation.

Early radial engines had their cylinders completely exposed to the air, but in the early 1930s a shaped ring cowling was added around the engine to improve air flow around the cylinders and reduce the drag caused by the wide, flat-fronted engine.

The main trouble with the air-cooled radial was that there was no fixed upper limit on its temperature, so it would overheat very quickly if overextended. This problem, however, led to the production of high-quality heat-resistant alloys which made the development of the high-performance jet engine possible later on.

Advances in design

The aero engine designers of the 1920s and 1930s had little of today's complex testing equipment, such as ULTRASONICS and SPECTROSCOPES. They managed, however, to produce reliable engines with ingenious new features by means of good design and careful workmanship.

One of the best of these improvements was the *sleeve valve*, which replaced the valve gear of a conventional engine with a single tube sliding up and down between the piston and the cylinder – it completely encircles the piston. It has ports, or holes, in its upper end. These slide past matching ports in the cylinder head which are connected to the fuel supply and exhaust systems, thus opening and closing them at the correct time. This greatly reduces the number of moving parts in the engine, particularly as the sleeve can be moved by quite simple machinery set around the inner edge of the ring of cylinders instead of the conventional long train of rods and levers reaching to the outside.

The alloy of which the sleeve is made is vital. If it expands too much as it heats up it jams against the cylinder; too little and it jams against the piston. Its designer, Roy Fedden, had to consult 60 firms before he found the right alloy.

Many engines had SUPERCHARGERS – compressors to force extra fuel and air into the cylinders and thus improve the engine's performance. These had been used as early as 1910, but were never entirely satisfactory because the compressor needed power to drive it, so wasting some of the extra power it gave. Several attempts were made to build a *turbo-supercharger* (turbocharger) powered by a TURBINE driven by the exhaust gases, but there was still no alloy that would withstand the high temperature. This was found later.

By the mid-1930s, engines were producing so much power that the propeller was being driven at an excessive speed. The tips of the blades broke the sound barrier and created shock waves that reduced the propeller's efficiency. The difficulty was overcome by gearing the propeller down. The more advanced American engines had variable gearing. By the end of the 1930s most propellers also had variable *pitch* (blade angle) so that they could run efficiently at different speeds.

There was always an incentive for designers to produce more and more powerful engines. During the 1920s and 1930s it was the glamorous (and lucrative) Schneider Trophy; later it was the desperate need to build fast aircraft in World War II.

Among the most famous engines of this long period of rapid development were the British Jupiter of 1921, a 9-cylinder radial producing 485 hp. This was one of Fedden's designs. In 1926, the American Pratt and Whitney Wasp, another 9-cylinder radial, produced 600 hp, and in 1929 the Wright Cyclone, another American radial 9, produced 1525 hp.

Meanwhile, Rolls-Royce produced a V-12 water-cooled engine for the Schneider Trophy which gave 2600 hp, though only for a few minutes at a time. This was all that was needed for two successful races, but the basic design of the short-lived engine was used for the famous Rolls-Royce Merlin, which powered the Spitfire, Hurricane and Mustang in World War II. The original 1934 Merlin produced only 790 hp, but by the end of the war this value had been considerably increased, to well over 2000 hp, by successive modifications.

Radial engines included the British Bristol Hercules of 1936, a 14-cylinder two-row radial that gave 1980 hp, and a long series of American Pratt and Whitney Wasp engines, such as the Double Wasp (1937; 2500 hp) and the Wasp Major, an amazing 28-cylinder 4-row radial (1945; 3800 hp). By this time, the piston aero engine had reached the end of its possibilities as an engine for large aircraft. It was used for years afterwards, and still is, for small aircraft, but leadership in design has passed to the jet engine and gas turbine.

See also: Aerospace industry; Airplane; Aviation; Internal combustion engine; Jet engine and gas turbine; Propeller, aircraft; Turbofan.

Left: Today's propeller-driven airliners, such as the British Aerospace 748, use turboprops instead of piston aero engines: not only are they lighter, quieter, and more free from vibration, but also more fuel efficient. A turboprop burns fuel like a jet engine, but the gases are used to power a compressor, which drives the propeller. In a jet engine, the gases are exhausted to provide thrust.

Aerosol spray can

First patented in the U.S. in 1941, aerosol spray cans have been used as convenient packages for an ever-increasing range of products including paints, cosmetics, insecticides, adhesives and foodstuffs.

A spray can is normally made of tinplate with soldered seams, though for products that are stored under high pressure an aluminum can is used. At the top, there is a simple plastic valve to control the spray. From the bottom of this, a flexible dip tube runs down to the bottom of the can.

The can is filled with the product to be sprayed and the propellant, a compressed gas such as butane or Freon. The gas is partly liquefied by the pressure in the can, but there is a layer of free gas above the liquid. As the can empties liquefied gas vaporizes to fill the space.

The valve is normally held shut by the pressure in the can, and by the coil spring directly below the valve stem. When the push button is pressed, it forces the valve stem down in its housing, uncovering a small hole which leads up through the stem to the nozzle in the button. This allows the product to be forced up the dip tube by the gas pressure in the can. The nozzle is shaped to give a spray or a continuous stream.

To produce a fine mist, a propellant is used which mixes with the product. The two leave the nozzle together and the propellant evaporates as soon as it reaches the air, breaking the product into tiny droplets. The same technique used with a more viscous liquid and a wider nozzle results in a foam. For a continuous stream of liquid or more viscous material, a nonmixing propellant is used, and the dip tube reaches into the product.

A different arrangement is used in cans containing very viscous substances. The product is enclosed in a plastic bag attached to the underside of the valve and the propellant fills the space between the bag and the can. This stops the product from sticking to the sides of the can.

Dangers

The widespread use of aerosol cans using Freon as the propellant led scientists to believe by the late 1970s that the ozone layer in the upper atmosphere, which filters out harmful ultraviolet radiation from the sun, could be destroyed by the large quantities of fluorocarbons in the gas being released into the air. Federal controls were introduced to ban the use of Freon, and other propellants are now employed, notably butane which, however, is dangerously flammable.

In 1985 a system using compressed air was introduced that solved the problem of decreasing air pressure in the can following each use, by employing an ingenious spring-loaded valve in the nozzle which keeps the pressure at the spray outlet constant and insures a smooth delivery.

See also: Airbrush; Canning; Food preservation; Packaging; Spray gun; Valve, mechanical.

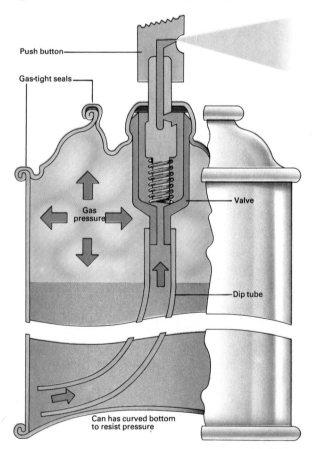

Push button
Gas-tight seals
Gas pressure
Valve
Dip tube
Can has curved bottom to resist pressure

Above: Aerosol can cutaway. Gas pressure created by the propellant forces liquid down the can and up the dip tube, emerging from the nozzle as a spray.

• FACT FILE •

- The aerosol spraying system has important medical uses. It is possible to dissolve drugs in an aqueous solution which can be atomized in an inhaler. The particles of drug solution are sufficiently small to enable a wide distribution over the internal surfaces of the lungs.

- In ink-jet printing, a combination of aerosol technique and electric charging of the droplets results in very accurate printing that can be carried out at high speed.

Aerospace industry

The aerospace industry today is responsible for the design and manufacture of civil and military aircraft, spacecraft, missiles, and aircraft-engines, and involves all of the world's major countries. Its activities include the regulation of safety and of operating standards, training of pilots and engineers, and maintenance of aircraft and equipment. Airports, airlines and the control of airspace are also a vital part of the industry.

Advances in digital electronics mean that the industry is changing rapidly. Computer aided design and manufacture is bringing about a revolution in aircraft production, the time needed for many of the complex operations often being cut by at least a half, while new materials and advanced techniques for improving the understanding of aerodynamics are helping to improve the performance and efficiency of aircraft.

Mass production

In the early days of flight, before World War I, aircraft were constructed entirely of wood, shaped and joined by skilled craftsmen, many of whom were drawn from other woodworking trades. Every aircraft was unique, and was the product of one person's thoughts on how best to achieve flight. The advent of World War I, however, brought a sudden need for thousands of aircraft, which meant that dedicated factories had to be built, and product techniques streamlined, enabling the large scale manufacture of components by unskilled workers.

This point is seen by many as the true beginning of the aerospace industry, when hitherto small companies grew into major manufacturers capable of turning out several types of aircraft, sometimes in huge numbers. British manufacturer Sopwith, for example, produced over 9000 Camels during the war, while in France over 8000 Spads were built.

While not so directly involved in World War I, America's embryonic aerospace industry was not far behind that of Britain and Germany, and was soon to outstrip both in its capacity for building aircraft. Many machines were supplied during the conflict, one of which, the Curtiss Jenny, was built in very large numbers.

The years between the wars saw a gradual change in the techniques for building aircraft. Designs

Below: Half airplane, half spacecraft, the Space Shuttle has been developed using techniques from the whole range of aerospace industries.

were improving as records continued to be set and broken, and wood and canvas gave way to aluminum as the principal structural material, monoplanes also becoming more popular than biplanes. Another important area of development was in aero engines, which became much more powerful and reliable. Aircraft also became an increasingly acceptable form of passenger transport as ranges and payloads increased and comfort improved.

The approach of the World War II meant that once more industry had to gear itself up to the mass production of aircraft and weapons. This time a great many more aircraft were produced, by Germany, Britain, the U.S., Italy and Japan. The aerospace industry had spread worldwide, and was to change dramatically in the five years leading to the end of hostilities. Piston aero engines became larger and more complex, and were produced in vast numbers, and the jet engine was developed and tested. The birth of radar, and the development of sophisticated electronics had also taken place, giving rise to the enormous avionics industries of today.

The huge demand for aircraft meant that aircraft manufacturers grew very large, so that when the war was over many companies in Britain and Europe were forced to shrink, or to join forces. Many disappeared altogether. In Britain, for example, great names such as Vickers, Avro, English Electric and Hawker Siddeley all eventually became part of

Above: Assembly of the Rolls-Royce Olympus 593 power plants for the Anglo/French supersonic airliner, Concorde, at the Rolls-Royce works.

British Aerospace, which today is one of the world's largest aerospace companies.

American manufacturers largely remained intact, since the demands of the U.S. military were growing, and air travel was becoming increasingly popular. The aerospace industry also diversified to include helicopters, spacecraft, and missiles.

Computerization

The industry today is made up of thousands of companies in the U.S., Europe, and Asia. Major changes have taken place during the last ten years or so, largely as a result of the development of digital computers and new production techniques. The design process has speeded up because designers can call upon computers to help choose the best materials, and insure that the individual parts are shaped in the best way for lightness and ease of manufacture. Many factories are now almost totally automated, the computers responsible for design being linked directly to those which guide the cutting tools. This means that the components of an aircraft or engine can be made very much more quickly than before, reducing production costs considerably, and enabling the manufacturer to respond more quickly to

Above: An assembly hall where engines are installed into Boeing airliners. The manufacture of conventional aircraft is one way to develop the expertise required to design and build spacecraft.

Right: Super-lightweight composite-material wings for the highly maneuverable Grumman X29 fighter plane are made as a single component on an old-fashioned jig, but use the very latest in aerospace technology to achieve high degrees of tolerance.

demand. It also helps the manufacturer to be more flexible, slowing production at times of low demand without having to lay off skilled workers.

An important trend in the aerospace industry is that many countries which previously had no choice but to buy their aircraft from the major Western manufacturers or from the Soviet Union, are now able to build their own. India, for example, has a rapidly developing industry, and is now capable of building under license almost any kind of aircraft or spacecraft. China is also building up its aerospace industry, importing technology from the West to help it to be self sufficient in aircraft production.

Collaboration

Another trend results from the enormous cost of developing aircraft. Manufacturers are increas-ingly forced to collaborate in new projects, one company building the wings, another the fuselage, and yet another the tailplane. In fact every part of the aircraft is often built by a different manufacturer, which specializes in development and production of that particular part.

The European Airbus Industrie consortium is an example, British Aerospace being responsible for supplying wings for all Airbus aircraft. Fuselages and empennage (tailplane and fin) are made in Europe, and the engines in the U.S.

Aero engines, which constitute about a quarter the cost of the whole aircraft, are also sometimes built by several companies joining together. The development cost of a modern aero engine is at least $1000 million, so it makes sense to spread the amount. Often several countries are involved. A

Avionics has become a major part of the aerospace industry, also today making up about a quarter the cost of the finished aircraft. The days of mechanical cockpit instruments are over, all new aircraft having digital computers that manage the incoming information on navigation, systems and engines and distribute it to the pilot on TV screens. Once again, specialized companies are responsible for the development of avionics, and they now represent a vital and growing segment of the industry.

New materials

New materials are now appearing which promise to change the shape of the aerospace industry for ever. Composites such as Kevlar, glass fiber and carbon fiber enable manufacturers to build aircraft that are closer to the ideal shape required by aerodynamics, and also much lighter. These materials are made into components, in a quite different way than is done with aluminum, the principal material of aircraft today. Wings and fuselages are laid up from layers of composite coated in resin, and cured in huge ovens, or autoclaves. The process takes place in a very clean, dust-free environment, a far cry from the traditional aircraft factory, where the sound of riveting and of huge machines cutting metal is always predominant. Several new business aircraft are now being constructed entirely from composites, use of the material in larger commercial and military aircraft being restricted to secondary structures only, such as wing leading edges or undercarriage doors.

One of the most rapidly developing sectors of the aerospace industry is in the exploitation of space. The decision in the U.S. to proceed with the construction of a space station provided a major challenge for companies in Europe as well as America, many of which collaborated to provide components of the station. Germany and Italy, for example, contributed some of the modules needed to provide living and working space for the scientists and astronauts taking part, and Britain developed a platform. In fact, the U.S. Skylab space station completed a highly successful mission, then burned up as it fell back into the Earth's atmosphere.

The use of satellites is also growing, many countries now wanting their own satellite for Earth resources observation, weather mapping and telecommunications. This demand has led to the development of the Space Shuttle re-usable launcher, and in Europe, the Ariane rocket, each of which can launch two satellites per mission at relatively low cost.

See also: Aero engine; Aircraft; Airplane; Airport; Aviation; Avionics; Head-up display; Inertial guidance; Jet engine and gas turbine; Missile; Pilotless aircraft; Space shuttle.

Above: The propeller makes a come-back. This propfan developed by the U.S. Space Agency, NASA, is an advanced means of propulsion that could pull an airplane through the air at speeds of nearly Mach 0.8. Each blade is designed to simulate a high-performance swept wing, and is in fact a cross between turbine, wing and propeller.

new engine now being designed for 150-seater aircraft is being developed by a group of seven companies in five countries – the U.S., Britain, West Germany, Italy and Japan. No one company could afford to develop the engine on its own, so each produces a number of components together constituting a complete module, which is sent to the final assembly line. The multinationally built aircraft also encourages a multinational market.

Agricultural technology

Of all the machines to be found on even the most technologically advanced farm today the tractor remains the most versatile. Since the first self-propelled models began superseding the horse on farms at the turn of this century the tractor and its many derivatives have revolutionized farming methods and changed the face of the landscape throughout the world.

The early tractors functioned chiefly for the purpose of heavy work, but the introduction of the light tricycle tractor in 1924 with its ability for easy maneuver, paved the way for greater versatility in tractor design, so they became useful in crop cultivation as well. This development heralded a new era for farming and it signaled the demise of the work horse on farms.

There are three main types of tractor in common use today. The rowcrop tractor is a lightweight design, featuring high ground clearance, adjustable wheel track widths, a small turning circle, good visibility and, as its name suggests, these features are especially useful for the operating of hoeing machinery close to row crops. Its engine power ranges between 30 to 45 hp. The general purpose tractor is heavier and more powerful (around 50–100 hp) and is used for most work on arable and livestock farms. It generally has heavy duty HYDRAULICS and drawbar for lifting considerable loads. The third type is the four-wheel drive tractor. These can be of two sorts. It may be big and powerful (up to 200 hp) with four equally large wheels. These models are best suited to plowing and heavy cultivation. The other four-wheel drive model has small front wheels, a less powerful engine (70–90 hp) and can be used as a general purpose tractor. The advantages of a four-wheel drive are its ability to utilize more power and the improved traction, flotation and stability it offers, making it an ideal tractor for wet and slippery weather conditions. In the U.S. and Canada large articulated four-wheel drives are commonly used. They can work fast, having engine powers of up to 350 hp and they can handle a wide range of implements.

Harvesting methods

Since the production of the first self-propelled cereal combine harvester in 1938 this impressive looking machine has proved by far the most popular method of harvesting in the West. Despite its high capital outlay farmers have found it a worthwhile investment or they have been prepared to employ combine

THE FORD FW FOUR-WHEEL DRIVE TRACTOR

1 Insulated cab	7 Axles
2 Air conditioning	8 Battery
3 Diesel engine	9 Transfer case
4 Instrumentation	10 Drive shaft
5 Gear selectors	11 Hitch
6 Transmission	12 High-traction tires

Left: The Ford FW four-wheel drive articulated tractor, typical of the new generation of versatile, general purpose work horses particularly suited to the large-scale farming of the U.S. and Canada. Most North American all-wheel-drive machines have equal-sized large-diameter wheels to give maximum grip for heavy pulling work across vast acreages.

STRAWBERRY HARVESTER

1 Pick-up reel
2 Reciprocating knife
3 Elevator
4 Conveyer
5 Air blast
6 Air fan
7 Rotating knife
8 Elevator

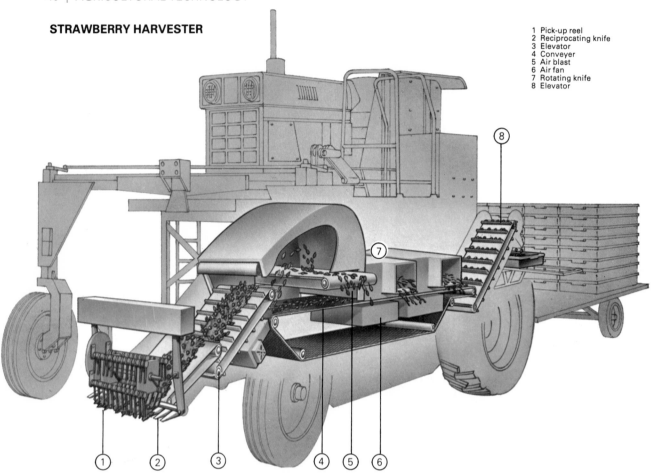

custom operators to cut their crop for them for a set fee per acre. Some operators follow the harvesting season from Texas to Canada carrying their enormous combines on flatbed trucks wherever road transport is necessary.

There are three types of plow. The fixed plow, which carries its moldboards on the right-hand side, the reversible plow which has moldboards on both sides of the plow body that can turn on the frame, either mechanically or hydraulically, and the disc plow. The reversible can plow up and down in the same furrow. Although expensive to buy, it saves time both in marking out and at headlands, as well as leaving a level field, leaving less work to be done in seedbed preparation. The disc plows are the most popular types in the U.S. where erosion by wind and water is often a problem. The discs, whether mounted on the right or reversible, replace the heavy-duty tillage of the moldboards and simply stir the soil, leaving it as well bound together as possible. Naturally this shallow tillage is less effective in burying weeds or crop residue. Where conservation of water and soil are a priority the practice of post-harvest plowing is sometimes replaced entirely by a stubbling mulching sweep which draws several knives through the ground, cutting

roots but leaving the soil barely affected. In some such cases it is considered wiser to leave the soil altogether undisturbed and plant directly into it. Intercropping is yet another technique used to combat the effects of erosion.

Seeding techniques

Almost every farmer growing crops in the Western world now uses seed drills rather than relying on the ancient practice of broadcasting, where seed distribution is quite random. The seed drill has been designed in order to avoid wastage of either seed or land. It consists of a hopper, which is filled with seeds, a series of tubes into which the seeds are mechanically channeled and a matching number of colters which cut small hollows in the ground into which the seeds are dropped. The seeds are generally gravity fed but pneumatic feeding, whereby the seed is guided by an airflow, is now considered to have advantages in distribution. Many farmers favor the use of the combine drill which drops seed and fertilizer together into a single cut. The dual operation can also be applied to no-till or direct drilling methods, when the seed is being planted into unplowed or uncultivated ground.

With such heavy demands on the land to produce

Left: Strawberry harvester separates fruit and foliage en route to the packing station. The machine lifts the plants, separates fruit from foliage, cuts stalks and carries berries to the packing boxes.
Right: Riding high in an English orchard, this apple picking machine is gentler than shaking the trees. Fingers along each side of the harvester probe the trees to pluck the fruit.

high and frequent yields intensive fertilizing is necessary. Systematic elimination of harmful pests or diseases is also fundamental to modern farming techniques. Chemicals for these purposes are distributed by sprayers, which consist of a tank, a pump, a control valve and a boom, along which are a number of nozzles. Liquid from the tank passes into the pump, which when attached to a tractor may be driven by its power takeoff or by a hydraulic motor. Pressure can be set by an adjustable relief valve to give the required application and excess liquid is returned to the tank, keeping the flow of chemicals and water well mixed. Filters are located throughout the mechanism and are designed to prevent blockages at the nozzles. Electronically controlled switches in the cab can regulate the application through the nozzles. Spray booms, which may be as wide as 60 ft (18m), generally fold on spring loaded hinges, which give when the boom hits an obstruction, thus reducing possible damage to the sprayer. Some sprayers are self-propelled and still others are carried by helicopter or airplane. Aerial application is particularly suited to very large farms but difficulties encountered in maintaining a uniform height can increase the risks of spray drift, causing possible damage to neighboring crops and water.

Chemical firms are at present experimenting with electrodynamic spraying techniques that are designed to aim droplets more accurately from a nozzle to a target crop, so reducing spray drift.

Mechanization now extends into every aspect of modern farming. There are power driven machines for driving fencing posts into the ground and for clearing manure from farm buildings. Farmyard equipment, such as grain driers and food mixers for animal feed, can be run by main electric power (which is usually cheaper at night) or by a farm's own generator.

Most livestock and poultry farming these days operates on a huge scale and is highly automated. With confinement and controlled conditions for animals and mechanized feeding systems operated from a single control shed, the farmer has virtually no labor costs to contend with and production is generally high. Dairy farming still requires rather more daily care and attention, though udder washing can now be done by automated spray jets and a cluster system (on milk machines) can disengage and hang itself up when milk flow ceases.

However, the high cost of mechanization to the farmer has encouraged specialization on the farm and the trend for large farms, MONOCULTURE and

Technology in agriculture. Top: Helicopters are used increasingly for large-scale crop dusting and foliage protection, as here against the Western Spruce budworm in Montana. Above: Experimental work in progress at a selective plant-breeding institute.

gauge the maximum speed at which a machine can move before its efficiency is impaired. The calculation is a complex one, depending on many factors. For example, ground speed, which until recently took no account of wheel slip in wet weather, was assessed simply by the number of wheel revolutions. This led to inaccuracies in many areas, including seed drilling. A sensor, which is unaffected by wheel slip, can now be fitted to the wheel of any self-propelled machine and transmit a true measurement of ground speed to the speedometer fitted in the cab. This information can then be linked to, for example, a seed drill operation. This, in turn, maximizes the efficiency of the drill, avoiding waste of land, seed and fuel. Sensors, in conjunction with other electronic instruments, can now measure grain yield on a combine harvester, shaft speeds on the power takeoff, grain moisture or flow quantity on a sprayer and monitors can signal to a driver any malfunctions of a machine by visual or audio alarms. In the case of combine driving, where the operator must be aware of many simultaneous operations, these automatic monitoring systems are of considerable value. Electronic linkages are also replacing mechnical ones, as the old types are subject to wear and consequently imprecision, and in the cabs consoles carrying switches, lights and dials are outmoding levers.

The real breakthrough in electronic research and development is in the area of microprocessing. Small instruments can now store information on a circuit etched onto a tiny piece of silicon and calculations can appear almost instantaneously on meters and dials. Because of the sensitivity of these instruments electronics have not previously been well suited to the muddy and bumpy field environment, but new methods of protection are being devised to make them available to the modern farmer. As electronic devises become smaller, cheaper and more robust, a demand for them will increase in the agricultural market.

Indeed computers and robots on the farm are already in the experimental stages. Australian researchers have built a sheep-shearing robot which takes 15 minutes to shear a single sheep, which is slow compared with its human counterpart – but of course it never gets tired. In Japan scientists have developed a computer-controlled, driverless combine for rice harvesting and the French are developing robot designs for picking grapes and fruit. Mobility and three-dimensional vision seem to be the major stumbling blocks in robot design but it is envisaged that they could be used to plant, cultivate and harvest.

intensive farming techniques may well have reached its peak. In many parts of the West overproduction of livestock and crops and their consequential drop in price on the world market is presenting new problems. The demand for more powerful machinery would appear to be at the point of giving way to a new concern: that of waste. Recent developments would seem to reflect this.

Where there is greater power it is possible to achieve higher speeds of operation, but for highspeed operations there must be a high degree of precision too. This function can be achieved by the use of electronic equipment, and this is the area in which greatest technological advances are at present being made for farm machinery. By means of sensors and monitors it has now become possible to

See also: Combine harvester; Cultivator; Dairy industry; Farming, intensive; Fertilizer; Irrigation techniques; Pest control; Plow.

Air

Air is a mixture of gases enveloping the Earth. Essentially, it is composed of one part oxygen to three parts nitrogen, along with smaller, variable quantities of water, carbon dioxide (CO_2), and the RARE GASES — helium, argon, krypton, neon, and xenon. Oxygen, nitrogen, water, and carbon dioxide are vital gases, but the other gases are equally important. Together, they form the atmosphere, which screens the Earth from lethal radiation.

Although the atmosphere extends outward some 620 miles (1,000 km) it is really only the first few miles (normally measured in thousands of feet) that are significant since three-quarters of the atmosphere's weight lies within 60,000 ft (18,000 m). It is well within this layer, usually from around 15,000 ft (4,500 m) down to the surface, that weather patterns occur because at these levels there are varying amounts of water vapor which condense into cloud formations. This layer is called the troposphere and meteorological conditions within it are affected by changes in temperature because the air gets progressively colder and thinner the higher it is. These changes in temperature also lead to changes in pressure, which cause large bodies of air to move from one location to another to cause the wind. The point at which temperature decline

Right: Air is a many-layered system enveloping and protecting Earth. Below: Spectacular sunsets are frequently seen in polluted industrial areas.

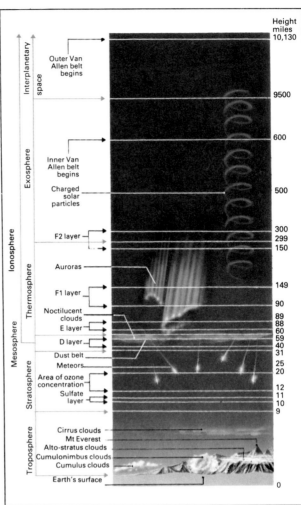

ceases is the tropopause, and the layer above this is the stratosphere. Ozone found in the upper part of this region, which extends to about 35 miles (56 km), protects the Earth from harmful ULTRAVIOLET radiation from the Sun.

The mesosphere separates the stratosphere from the ionosphere, which begins at about 34 miles (55 km). In the ionosphere there is no protective ozone layer to block solar radiation so that the atmospheric molecules are bombarded with ultraviolet rays, becoming electrically charged, or ionized. It is this ionized layer which reflects radio waves down to Earth, and enables long distance signals and communications to be bounced round the Earth instead of being launched into space.

Origins

To begin with, the Earth had no atmosphere, being an extremely hot volcanic planet devoid of life. Gradually, beginning about 3 thousand million years ago, the Earth began to cool. As it did so, the gases and steam that previously escaped into space were held back by the Earth's gravity, and the

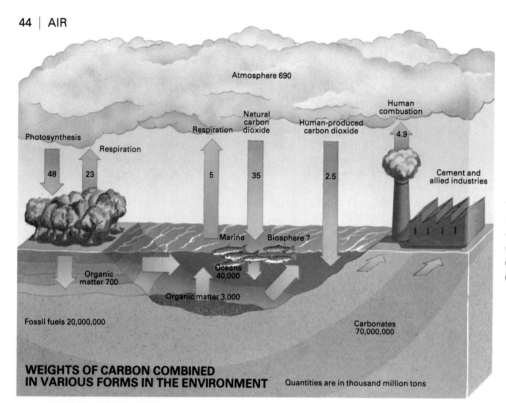

Left: The carbon dioxide cycle, and how it is threatened by humans. Excess CO_2 can be removed from the atmosphere by processes in the carbon cycle, but it is constantly being replaced by carbon unlocked from the ground through burning fossil fuels and chemical processing, especially of mineral carbonates - as in cement production.

WEIGHTS OF CARBON COMBINED IN VARIOUS FORMS IN THE ENVIRONMENT Quantities are in thousand million tons

steam condensed to form the primordial oceans. An atmosphere of nitrogen and carbon dioxide formed providing the basis for life to develop.

Photosynthesis, which is the manufacture of organic compounds (such as sugar and starch) from inorganic substances (like water and carbon dioxide) by living plant cells using the energy of sunlight absorbed by the plant pigment CHLOROPHYLL, led to large quantities of oxygen being breathed into the atmosphere by plants. With oxygen in the atmosphere, animal life was able to develop which in turn uses oxygen as fuel and produces carbon dioxide and nitrogen as waste for the plants to feed on, and the balance was complete.

However, not only animals but automobile and airplane engines, industrial processes and the large scale clearance of oxygen-producing, nitrogen-consuming forests all have an effect on the ecological balance, putting an ever greater strain on the green plants to supply the nutrients necessary to keep the relative quantities of oxygen and carbon dioxide as well as nitrogen in the air constant.

Light

The composition of air has a noticeable effect on the way in which visible light reaches the surface of the Earth. Like X rays or gamma rays, visible light is a form of electromagnetic radiations which travel uninterrupted through space and easily through air on a bright, clear day. However, if there are particles of water vapor or dust in the atmosphere, the light can become scattered or absorbed leading to sometimes spectacular effects such as a rainbow or

the colorful sunsets often seen in heavily industrial areas, or following volcanic activity which throws quantities of blue light-absorbing particles into the upper atmosphere, coloring the sun and sky red. Similarly, sound is transmitted through the air – it cannot travel in space. The cause of a sound, such as a clapper striking the side of a bell, causes particles in the immediate vicinity to vibrate, pushing and pulling or compressing and decompressing the air outward from the source in a series of waves which can be detected by the eardrum that echoes these vibrations, perceived by the brain as sound. The speed of sound is affected by air temperature so that it moves more slowly through cold, heavier air.

Measurement

Windspeed is calibrated in miles per hour and is calculated by an anemometer, while the amount of water vapor in the atmosphere is measured with a hygrometer. Air temperature is measured in degrees Fahrenheit or Celsius, using a thermometer placed out of direct sunlight. However, probably the commonest means of measuring air is to measure its pressure, which is directly related to relative humidity and temperature, using a barometer, which is most commonly expressed in millibars or atmospheres. At sea level, atmospheric pressure is equal to 14.69 pounds per square inch.

See also: Aerodynamics; Air conditioning; Anemometer; Atom and molecule; Barometer; Earth; Gas laws; Geophysics; Gravitation; Light; Meteorology; Nitrogen; Oxygen.

Airbrush

An airbrush is a versatile, precision instrument capable of producing finely detailed, illustrative paintwork. Developed originally in the 1920s from a tool used for retouching monochrome photographs, the airbrush works by passing compressed air over a reservoir of paint, which is sucked out in a fine spray.

Regulating screws and levers on the airbrush are used to adjust the paint texture and fan profile as it leaves the nozzle cap, so that a range of effects can be achieved. Unlike a spray gun, the airbrush nozzle cap is not usually adjustable, though on some models it is removable and a cap of different profile can be substituted to vary the effects.

The paint is diluted with thinners, and the airbrush body has a valved adapter through which compressed air is supplied, either from an aerosol can or an electrically driven compressor.

The simplest type of airbrush works by a single action trigger lever. When the lever is depressed it allows compressed air to escape from the reservoir, through the body of the airbrush and out through a fine nozzle at the front. This gas jet blows across the opening of the paint pot and draws paint up through it. Thus an atomized spray is produced which is directed on to the workpiece, controlled by the amount of pressure applied to the trigger.

The simplest airbrushes are really only suitable for touch-up work, as they cannot be controlled for the accuracy needed for complex paint jobs.

The more sophisticated type of airbrush has a double action trigger lever, which allows a flow of gas when it is depressed and a flow of paint regu-

Below: A double-action airbrush, a particularly precise instrument requiring much skill to master. The gun section can be screwed down onto a reservoir can containing any type of paint, usually mixed with thinners to help it emerge as a fine spray.

lated by a needle when it is pulled back. The operator can control these actions to vary the thickness of the paint spray to achieve any desired pattern of spray and so regulate the desired finish of the work with a high degree of precision.

Painting materials

To use an airbrush well requires much practice, and the types of materials used are just as important to the final finish as the actual techniques of applying the medium.

The type of colorant to be applied will obviously depend on where the finished result will be used. To custom paint a car or bike, for example, normal or acrylic lacquers are best suited. Other mediums include ink, water color, gouache and enamels, each giving a different effect.

Most airbrushed designs are made by progressive masking, which is blanking off the areas that do not want painting with a particular color. Masking materials include tape, masking paper, stencils and frisk film.

Narrow masking tape is ideal for intricate designs and the wider tapes can be used with masking paper to mask off larger areas.

Stencils can be made by cutting a design in a piece of card then spraying through it to lay the design on the surface to be painted.

Frisk film is transparent plastic sheeting with a slight adhesive on one side. The design is drawn on the area to be painted and the frisk film applied on the top. Then, areas to be sprayed are carefully cut out with a sharp blade, taking care not to score through the underlying surface.

As with the different types of pigment used, the height that the airbrush is held from the paper or panel will also determine the density of the medium sprayed over the area to be covered.

See also: **Aerosol spray can; Air; Compressor; Mixture; Paint manufacture; Photographic processing; Reproduction, printing; Spray gun.**

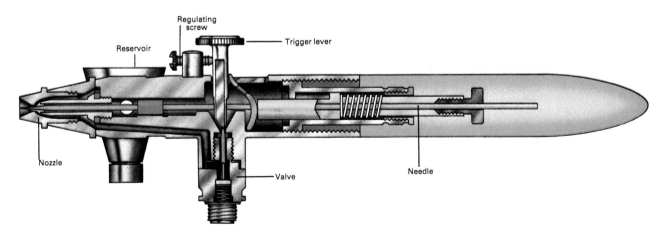

Regulating screw

Trigger lever

Reservoir

Nozzle

Valve

Needle

Air conditioning

Air conditioning is the creation of an artificial climate, making it possible to maintain constant, pleasant conditions inside buildings and provide a steady flow of purified air.

Air conditioning is essential in underground spaces, movie theaters, dance halls, crowded stores, hospitals, tall office buildings, and in many industrial processes which are sensitive to atmospheric conditions.

Methods used

Air is purified, cooled or heated, humidified or dried, according to the need, by the air conditioning plant and circulated through the building by means of ducts, which may be of metal or may be formed out of the structure itself.

There are various stages in a large air conditioning plant: not all plants include every component, and in the smallest air conditioning unit the components are combined in one casing not much larger than a television set.

Air first enters a section where it mixes with recycled air from the building – only a certain proportion of fresh air is needed. Next, the mixed air passes through a filtering section, which may be in two stages. The first stage takes out coarse dust, and will be a fibrous medium, rather like cotton, either in the form of a screen of individual filter cells which can be replaced when they become dirty, or an electrically driven roller screen. Following this is the second stage filter which is generally an electrostatic type and removes the finer particles such as cigarette smoke. In this, a high voltage is used to charge incoming dust particles which are then attracted to a grid of oppositely charged plates.

The air temperature is controlled by passing the air through two tube banks. One is supplied with hot water or steam, and the other with chilled water or a refrigerant fluid. Inside the room to be ventilated is a temperature sensor – usually an electric resistance thermometer – which is set to the desired value. The difference between the required and the actual temperature automatically determines whether the heating or cooling tubes are used.

The next stage is the odor filter, made of activated

Below: Air leaves the room through an exhaust duct and is mixed with fresh air from outside before being passed through filters, cooling and heating tubes, an odor filter and a humidifier, and finally a silencer. Many units can heat as well as cool the air.

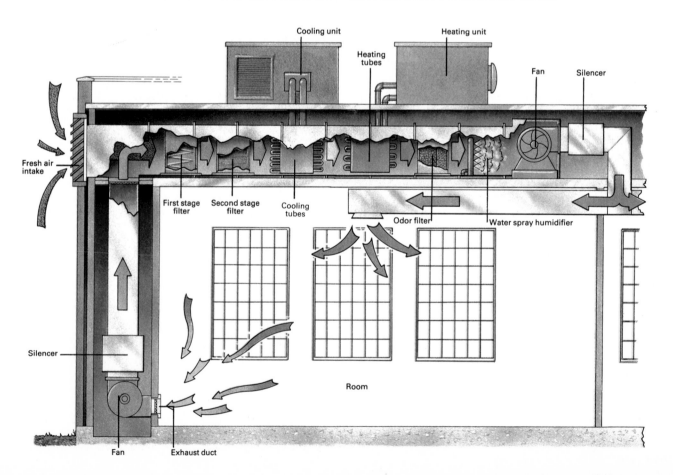

carbon, a substance which is capable of directly absorbing odor molecules from the air. This needs to be reactivated by heating from time to time to drive off the absorbed material.

Finally, moisture is added to produce the desired humidity, either by injecting steam into the air or by spraying a mist of very fine water droplets. This too is controlled from a sensor inside the room, the electric resistance of which varies with the humidity. If moisture has to be removed from the air, the usual method is to arrange for it to be both cooled and then reheated if necessary at the temperature control stage. The moisture will condense on the cooling tubes.

The air is normally moved through the system by a centrifugal fan, the rotor of which resembles a paddle wheel. Air enters at the center and leaves around the edge of the wheel. This type of fan can move large volumes of air despite the appreciable drag of the plant and ducting.

Silencers are always placed after the fan to prevent the noise of the plant from reaching the room. These usually consist of a labyrinth of sound absorbing material.

Air is finally delivered through metal ducts to the room diffusers. These take various forms, such as long slots or grilles in the walls close to the ceiling, vaned outlets flush with the ceiling, or perforated sections of the ceiling itself.

Air conditioning systems
The same principles are used from the smallest to the largest system. Small room units contain a simple washable filter, refrigerating compressor, and electric air heater.

More powerful units are made to supply larger rooms, and frequently the relatively noisy refrigerating section (compressor and condenser) is placed outside the building.

For large buildings there are three main systems: *all air, air–water,* and *all water.* In the first, the plant supplies all the air that is needed at a fixed temperature. Local duct heaters are needed in different rooms or zones of a building to give final temperature control. An alternative is to have two ducts, one carrying cool air, the other warm air. The two air streams are blended, as in a mixer faucet, to give the required temperature. In the variable volume system, the temperature is regulated by controlling the amount of air supplied instead of its temperature.

In the air–water system, the central plant only delivers the minimum fresh air needed for ventilation. Each room then has a separate heating and cooling unit using heated or chilled water. In the all water system, only the heating or cooling water is supplied from the central plant, and fresh air is brought in through room ventilators.

Above: Installing a reverse-cycle sliding-chassis heat pump unit like this requires only basic skills and is suitable for small commercial and private users.

Air conditioning today
Air conditioning is being used widely at the moment for office buildings, shops, supermarkets, restaurants, and entertainment centers, where the main problem is to keep the building cool in summer. Temperatures in modern buildings can become uncomfortably high through heat from lights, crowds of people, and sunshine through increasingly large windows.

The heat from artificial lighting is sometimes sufficient to keep a building warm in winter, and some buildings have been specifically designed to do just that: the hot air generated by the lights is picked up and returned to the plant.

In medicine, air conditioning is essential for the operating room. In this case the air must be sterile and must keep the area around the operating table free from contamination. In industry, air conditioning is needed to control the environment to a process or product. In so-called *white rooms*, for example, in the manufacture of TRANSISTORS, the atmosphere is cleaner than ever occurs naturally.

The largest single space ever air conditioned is the vehicle assembly building at Cape Canaveral in Florida: 525 ft (160 m) high and nearly 500 ft (150 m) square. The cooling power is sufficient to turn 7500 tons of water into ice in a day. There is even a plan to install a super efficient external air conditioning system in a major commercial center in Palm Springs.

See also: Air; Building techniques; Heat exchanger; Pollution control; Refrigeration; Thermometry; Thermostat; Ventilation; Water.

Aircraft

Aircraft is a generic term for any aerial vehicle, whether heavier or lighter than air. For the purposes of identification all aircraft can be broken down into four main categories, though there are a variety of different subcategories which go on to define the vast range of machines flying today. These basic categories are *aerostats* – aircraft that are lighter than air such as balloons or blimps, *gliders*, which are motorless airplanes, *airplanes* (by far the largest group) and *rotorcraft* meaning helicopters and autogiros.

Airships

Airships are lighter-than-air craft using a large envelope filled with gas to provide lift. Passengers and crew ride in a gondola suspended under the envelope. Engines are attached to either side of the gondola, and usually drive propellers or fans turning inside cowls, or ducts.

Airships are coming back into popularity owing to the use today of helium as the lifting gas instead of hydrogen, which is highly flammable, and caused several disasters. Helium is slightly heavier than hydrogen, but is completely safe. Airships also now benefit from new materials for making the envelope much lighter and tougher than before, and less prone to leakage.

Airships today are mostly of the nonrigid type, in which the gas envelope is self-supporting, as in an ordinary balloon. Early airships were built with a complex metal frame for the envelope, which took a long time to build and was very expensive.

The most modern airship now flying is built by Airship Industries in Britain, and features engines that can be rotated to assist with take-off and maneuver. Much interest is being shown by several countries in the use of airships for maritime surveillance and offshore patrol and rescue work, as well as transporting people and cargo.

Above: Balloons lifted by hot air or gas are becoming a popular sport once again. Balloons are aerostats, able to fly by being lighter than air.

Gliders

Unpowered airplanes designed to achieve maximum lift so that they can remain in the air for long periods. Today, they are used principally for sport flying, but towed gliders played an important role in World War II, carrying specialist troops to forward positions.

Most gliders today are made entirely from advanced composite materials, and are very light and strong. To create as much lift as possible, wings have to be extremely long, and thin, sometimes spanning as much as 70 ft (21 m).

Some gliders are fitted with lightweight motors, enabling take-off without help from a winch or towing airplane. These are generally called motor-gliders, and are used more for pleasure than sport.

Left: A modern airship, or blimp, currently seeing a postwar revival with the wider availability of helium as opposed to hydrogen, which caused several disasters in the early years. Modern blimps tend to be nonrigid dirigibles, meaning the gas bags are self-supporting but the aircraft is powered and can be steered.

Left: A sailplane or glider is capable of staying aloft for many hours, using its high lift-to-weight ratio and the upward currents or thermals generated by ground and weather conditions.
Below: right: Air-launched U.S. Tomahawk Cruise missile, basically a pilotless airplane with a wealth of complicated radar guidance and computerized memory systems on board, plus a deadly load.

Above: Replica Fokker DR1 triplane, one of the best known German fighter planes of World War I, in the all-red livery made famous by the ace Freiherr Manfred von Richtofen in the late part of the war.

Airplane

The first true airplane was built and flown by the Wright Brothers in 1903. Powered by an 8 hp engine, the Wright Flyer achieved the very first level flight over a distance of 120 ft (37 m).

The shape and performance of airplanes has changed considerably since then, because of advances in materials and aerodynamics, and the introduction of computers. The principles of flight, however, have remained the same.

Most of the lift is generated by the wing, which is located at the aircraft CENTER OF GRAVITY. The faster the aircraft moves forward, the more lift is produced. On its own, a lifting wing is unstable, tending to tip over forward as it advances. A tailplane is therefore needed to prevent this happening, and this is usually located at the rear of the aircraft. Pitch control (up and down) is achieved by elevators hinged to the tailplane trailing edge.

To give the airplane stability in the longitudinal plane, a vertical fin is required. This is also placed at the rear of the fuselage, forming a right angle with the tailplane. Hinged to the fin trailing edge is the rudder, which provides yaw control (movement left and right).

Devices to roll the airplane are needed, and these are located at the outer ends of the wings. They are called ailerons, and work differentially, so that one moves up while the other moves down. A turn to the left, for example, is accomplished when the left aileron moves up and the right one moves down.

The wing also carries the flaps, which are extended to increase wing area, and hence lift during take-off and landing.Wing lift is also increased by the use of leading edge slats. When

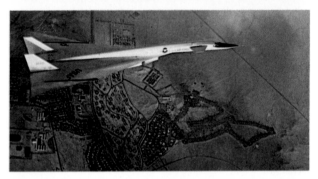

Top: A World War II Supermarine Spitfire XVI of the RAF, one of the most famous airplanes of the period. Center: The supersonic XB70 experimental aircraft, originally designed as a bomber. Above: A Naval Sea King helicopter deploys its sonar equipment.

extended, these cause air to flow faster over the wing's top surface.

All airplanes have engines designed to produce the maximum power for the minimum weight. Piston engines were predominant until the end of World War II, when turbine engines became popular because of their greater simplicity, efficiency and much higher power.

Almost all airplanes are today built from aluminum, although lightweight composite materials such as glass fiber and Kevlar are increasingly used in parts of the aircraft that are not structurally critical. An existing new research aircraft has, however, an all-composite wing that is swept forward instead of back to improve aerodynamic performance. The Grumman X-29, which flew for the first time in early 1985, points the way to fighters having far superior performance to those of today.

The most unusual operational airplane in the world is probably the Harrier/AV8 vertical take-off close support aircraft, in which four rotating nozzles direct exhaust air down and to the rear from a single turbine. Developed 17 years ago in Britain and in service with the RAF and Royal Navy, the Harrier has also been adopted by the U.S. Marines as the AV8 and has undergone considerable development in the U.S., and been used to great effect in combat.

Rotorcraft

A versatile aircraft capable of vertical take-off and hovering. Lift is produced by up to six rotating wings, or blades, hinged to a shaft driven by one, two, or even three engines via a transmission.

The whirling main rotor produces a torque effect that tries to rotate the helicopter around the main shaft. To react against this a tail rotor is fitted, geared to the main shaft. Its blades can be varied in pitch by the rudder pedals so that the amount of reaction can be varied according to the torque produced by the main rotor. In most helicopters, the complete propulsion system is mounted on top of the cab. Turbine engines are used almost universally, driving rotor blades made from advanced composite materials.

Helicopters have three main controls. The collective pitch lever, similar to the brake lever in an automobile, is used to adjust the pitch angle of the main rotor blades, and hence the lift. The lever is raised for take-off, and lowered for landing. The cyclic pitch lever is a stick in front of the pilot that controls forward motion and hover. It is used together with the tail rotor pedals, which behave in a similar way to the rudder in an airplane, by adjusting the orientation of the rear fuselage as the helicopter banks to port or starboard.

The operation of the main rotor blades is complex, since their ANGLE OF ATTACK must be varied according to the required speed and direction of the helicopter. For forward motion the blades must produce more lift as they pass over the rear of the fuselage, and less as they pass over the front, so that they effectively push air rearwards, and the helicopter forward.

A well known feature of many helicopters is the ability to fly sideway, or even backward. This is useful for precise positioning during air–sea rescue operations and for carrying heavy external loads.

Left: Ultralight and minimum aircraft are becoming increasingly popular as an alternative to relatively expensive light aviation flying. The Solar Challenger took the concept of low-cost aviation a stage further by crossing the English Channel in 1981 driven by a propeller powered by solar energy from wing panels, or photovoltaic cells in a bid to save fuel.

Many new designs are emerging which dramatically increase helicopter performance. One of these, the X-wing, achieves some of the virtues of an aircraft by locking the blades for forward flight so that they behave like the wings of an ordinary airplane. Another is the Advancing Blade Concept proposed in which two sets of blades rotate in opposite directions, thereby eliminating the need

Below: An autogiro derives its forward motion from a small pusher type propeller motor, and its lift from a free-rotating blade.

for a separate tail rotor, to counterbalance.

One new design, the Tilt Rotor, is truly half helicopter, half airplane, and is already flying. Engines attached to the wingtips each drive large, three-bladed rotors, and can be swiveled horizontally or vertically. The Tilt Rotor can fly twice as fast as a helicopter, and yet land in a small space.

See also: Aerodynamics; Aero engine; Aerospace industry; Air; Airplane; Airship; Aviation; Avionics; Glider; Helicopter; Jet engine and gas turbine; Propeller, aircraft; Wind tunnel.

Air cushion vehicle

Air cushion vehicles (ACVs) – also known as hover-craft or as ground effect machines (GEMs) – are vehicles which, when in motion, are supported by a layer of air, rather than by wheels or other direct means of contact with the passing surface.

This absence of contact with the surface has brought the advantages of both adaptability and speed: the latter is particularly well demonstrated when the ACV is compared with the conventional ship. For example, the large passenger ACV, the 305-ton SR.N4 Mk3 Super-4, is capable of speeds of 65 knots (120 km/h). The top speed for a crack liner is 35 knots (65 km/h). There are a number of reasons why this is so. First, in a conventional ship that area of the hull which is normally submerged is subjected to drag as a result of the VISCOSITY of the water through which it travels. Drag absorbs a good deal of engine power.

Second, wave formations are set up at bow and stern of a ship when it is under way. Again, this wave making process means a drain on the power

supply. Although this factor is less important than drag at low speeds, as speed increases it takes over as the major power wastage problem.

Finally, there are natural phenomena of currents and also of windage on the exposed areas of hull and superstructure.

Considering the first two factors alone, it can be appreciated that the bigger and faster the ship, the larger the amount of energy wasted. There comes a point when the cost of deriving more speed from a ship outweighs the advantages – unless there are special military or research factors.

Since none of the ACV is immersed it has none of these problems. At low speeds a wave making process is set up, but at cruising speeds this disappears. So though the ACV is affected by adverse winds, it

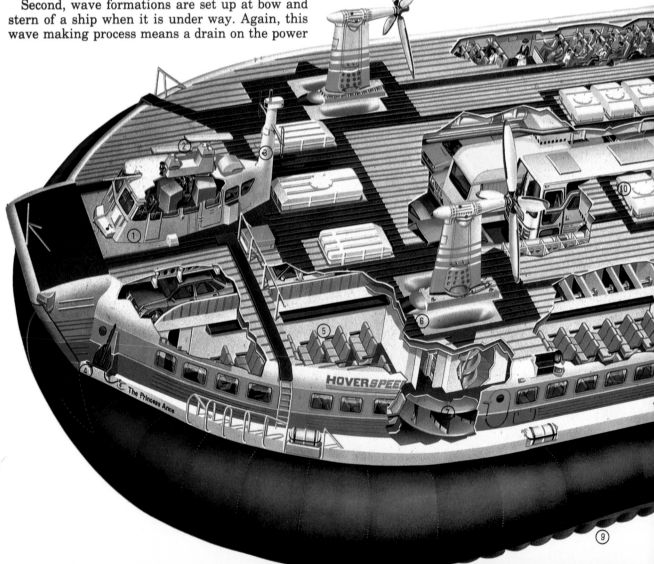

is generally faster not only than a conventional vessel of the same size but also larger ships.

In principle the ACV works as follows. The hull can be thought of as being something like an upturned tea tray with raised edges. If such a structure were placed carefully on the surface of water, a quantity of air would be trapped beneath it, retained by the edges which would now be jutting downward. If, however, you tried to propel the tray through the water, the air would escape and the tray would sink. Even if that did not happen, the submerged portions of the edges would be subjected to friction and would set up waves.

The pioneer designers were faced with two problems: how to raise the craft clear of the water, and how to keep the air cushion in place.

They overcame the first by ducting air into the cushion compartment at pressure a little higher than atmospheric, and the second by arranging a system of air jets around the edge to provide a curtain of air which slowed down the rate of leakage from the cushion. This system was improved by the

Below: The British Hovercraft Corporation SR.N4 Mk. 3 is a large passenger and vehicle carrying ACV. Hovercraft of this type are in regular service across the English Channel.

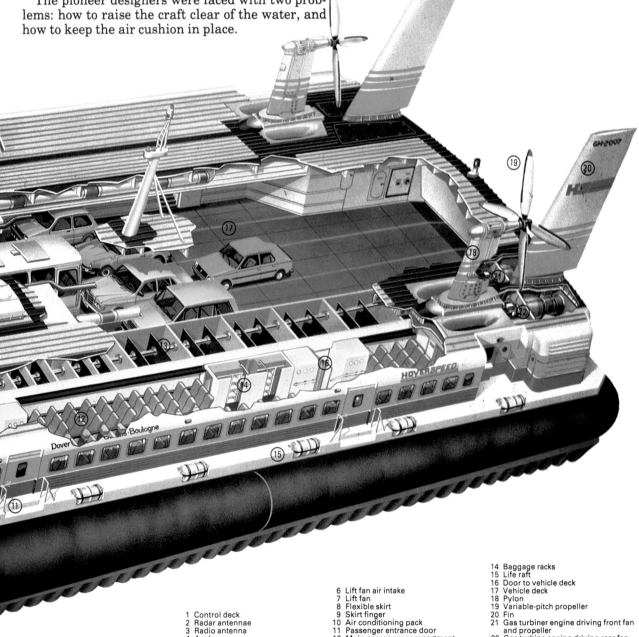

1 Control deck	14 Baggage racks
2 Radar antennae	15 Life raft
3 Radio antenna	16 Door to vehicle deck
4 Anchor	17 Vehicle deck
5 Forward passenger compartment	18 Pylon
6 Lift fan air intake	19 Variable-pitch propeller
7 Lift fan	20 Fin
8 Flexible skirt	21 Gas turbiner engine driving front fan and propeller
9 Skirt finger	22 Gas turbine engine driving rear fan and propeller
10 Air conditioning pack	
11 Passenger entrance door	
12 Main passenger compartment	
13 Drive shaft to front propeller and fan	

Left: The low-noise BHC AP. 1–88 diesel engine hovercraft entered service in 1983, and is considerably quieter than its gas turbine-powered rivals.

Above: An SR.N5 in service with the British Army in Malaya, where vehicles of this type were well suited to jungle and swamp conditions. They carry a payload of 18 passengers, or up to 2 tons commercial freight.
Left: A U.S. Navy air cushion vehicle leaves on a patroling mission in the Mekong Delta during the war in Indochina.

addition of a flexible skirt around the vessel's edge.

It has been calculated that a pressure of only about 60 lb/sq ft (300 kg/m²) is required to raise an ACV of 100 ton or more to a height of 1 ft (0.3 m). The pressure required to inflate car tires is a good deal greater.

Types of ACV

Several variations of the basic ACV principle have been evolved. The simplest is called the *air-bearing* system. Air is blown through a central orifice in the undersurface and leaks away outward in all directions from under the flexible retaining skirt.

The *plenum chamber* vessel has a concave under-surface, and the cavity forms the upper section of a cushion chamber which is completed by the sea or ground surface. Again the air leaks away under the edges of the retaining skirt.

In the *momentum curtain* system a ring of air jets is set around the circumference of the underside of the ACV. The air from these jets is directed down-ward and inward to retain the air cushion. This system has been further developed to include two rows of peripheral jets, one inside the other. The

Above: The Voyageur ACV was developed in Canada to operate in virtually any type of terrain and has a 25 ton freight capacity.

retaining air is blown out through one set, sucked up by the other after it has done its job, and then recirculated. This makes for greater efficiency, because it slows down the rate of air escape.

ACV propulsion systems have also been varied. The most popular for large vessels has been the airscrew or propeller. In the earliest machines, the fans that provided lift also drove air through a system of ducts to the stern where it was ejected for propulsion. In SR.N4, the four engines that drive the lift fans also drive external airscrews for propulsion. In many other types, the lift and propulsion systems are separately powered. Some ACVs even have water propellers. These cannot go on land.

The problems of steering an ACV are very similar to those of steering an airplane. As the ACV has no contact with sea or land there is a danger of drift during turns. The helmsman overcomes this by banking, or tilting his machine like an aircraft. He does so by reducing pressure from the air jets on the side which he wants to dip. Directional control is exerted by varying the power of the airscrew, by using the tail fins, or with both systems.

Development
The air cushion principle has fascinated designers for many years. Pioneering attempts at its use were made, for example, as far back as the 1930s, in both the U.S. and Finland. But it was not until after World War II that the real breakthrough came.

The inventor of the first successful ACV was Britain's C. S. Cockerell. Originally trained as an engineer and in electronics, he later turned his atten-

Above: A Soviet gas-turbine powered hovercraft operating tourist passenger services along the river Volga, to the Caspian Sea.

tion to the problems of boat and hovercraft design.

He tried at first to retain an air cushion under a boat by fitting hinged flaps at the bow and stern of his craft between side keels.

Finding this technique to be ineffective, he replaced the flaps with sheets of water pumped vertically downward. Air containment was still not very efficient, and finally he struck on the idea of using peripheral air jets for the purpose.

The world's first hovercraft, the SR.N1, was unveiled in 1959 when it traveled from the Isle of Wight to mainland England. Only a few weeks later it crossed the English Channel in two hours, and in 1965 the world's first regular passenger service was set up between the Isle of Wight and the mainland. Now a fleet of SR.N4s carries passengers and cars

regularly to and from France, and in 1982 captured 20 per cent of the total traffic.

In 1983, an entirely new type of hovercraft, the BHC AP.1-88, went into service between Ryde on the Isle of Wight and Southsea in England. Instead of having a hull which is riveted together, like an aircraft fuselage, it has a welded aluminum hull, and in place of the more usual gas-turbine engines it is powered by four Deutz 428 hp air-cooled marine diesel engines. Two of these drive the lift fans, and two drive the two ducted propellers at the rear of the craft via toothed rubber belts. The AP.1-88 is much quieter and cheaper to run than a gas-turbine powered craft of equivalent size.

The AP.1-88 is 77 ft (23.55 m) long and 33 ft (10.1

Left and above: This air cushion transporter spreads the load of heavy weights evenly across a cushion of air, able to move over 200 tons.

m) wide, and is capable of carrying up to 101 passengers (depending on seating arrangements) at speeds of up to 58 knots (107 km/h). It can be adapted to carry freight or vehicles for either civil or military purposes. A second AP.1-88 service, linking Malmo in southern Sweden with Copenhagen's Kastrup International Airport, began in 1984.

Uses of ACVs

The ACV has truly arrived as a means of providing high-speed transport over a variety of terrains. Because the air cushion acts not only as a form of support but also as an effective spring, the modern ACV can cope with waves of up to 10 ft (3 m) and can operate over rough ground as well. It has been used for military purposes by the U.S. armed forces in Vietnam and elsewhere in the Far East.

The advantages of this type of craft in naval warfare are considerable. It is not only speedy, but the larger types can deliver torpedoes and other missiles with telling effect. At the same time, since they are not in contact with the sea themselves, they are immune to torpedo attack.

The air cushion also shields the ACV from the effects of underwater explosions, which is obviously of use in mine clearance. Using minehunting sonar equipment to detect mines, and remote controlled mine disposal equipment, a minehunting and disposal ACV can operate continuously for up to three days at speeds of up to 5 knots.

There is also the whole area of ACV application on dry land. The concept has been used in the design of several devices including a type of lawn mower, a hoverpallet for transporting heavy loads around the factory, and enormous craft like the U.S. ACT 375, designed to carry a 375-ton payload.

See also: Aerodynamics; Hydrodynamics; Hydrofoil; Marine propulsion; Seaplane & amphibian.

• FACT FILE •

- Probably the world's biggest user and developer of hovercraft is the Soviet Union, which services the communities along the 5000 miles (8000 km) of coast between Murmansk and Vladivostock with an estimated 10,000 surface-effect ships.

- The U.S. Navy, needing large, fast combat and support ships, is experimenting with diesel and gas-turbine powered hovercraft capable of 80 knots (135 Km/h), and weighing up to 13,000 tons. Even these are exceeded in size by the planned East German Atlant nuclear-powered ferry, with space on board for 4,000 passengers and 2000 vehicles designed to cross the Atlantic in two days.

- In Canada an air-cushion-assisted golf cart has been developed. In wet conditions the hover mechanism reduces the weight on the wheels, enabling the cart to be used throughout the year.

Air lock

The air lock is a chamber designed to allow movement between compartments containing air at different pressures, or between a pressurized or vacuum compartment and the outside atmosphere with a higher or lower pressure.

A very common application, and one which demonstrates the principle involved, is its use in the *caisson*. This device is used for carrying out work on submerged bridge foundations, harbor structures, and so on. It consists of a wide vertical tube which reaches from the surface to the work site.

To keep the tube free of water for the workers, the pressure of the air inside must be maintained at the same level as that of the water around its lower end – inevitably greater than the surface air pressure.

This could be achieved by simply sealing the top of the caisson with an airtight trap door and pumping air inside to the necessary pressure. However, as soon as anyone attempted to open the trap in order to enter or exit, the pressurized air inside would rush out. Water would then flood the caisson.

The problem is overcome by having two airtight trap doors with a space between – the air lock. If a worker wishes to leave, valves between the work area and air lock are opened, equalizing the air pressure on each side.

The worker can then climb the ladder to the lock and enter, closing the trap door and valves behind to seal the work chamber again.

If workers do not need to undergo decompression, they can open the upper door and let themselves out. In this case, some of the high-pressure air will rush out, but that in the work chamber will be unaffected in any way.

If decompression is needed, then the pressure level in the lock is gradually reduced to atmospheric level by venting it through a set of valves in the upper door.

The journey is accomplished in reverse in very much the same way, except that the air in the lock will be at surface pressure when the workers enter. So, after the door is closed behind them, the air pressure in the lock is pumped up until it is equal in pressure with the work chamber, allowing them to take the next step.

Tunnel air locks

Similar air locks are employed in the construction of tunnels which run under the sea bed or under rivers. High-pressure air is pumped into the work area to keep the water out, and pressure is maintained by a bulkhead.. This air lock is the walk-through type, with an airtight door at each end, on either side of the bulkhead.

A further version of the air lock is used in sub-

Above: Astronaut meets cosmonaut in the docking module airlock between Apollo and Soyuz spacecraft during a joint U.S./Soviet mission.
Right: The airlock connecting the mid deck crew area of a space shuttle with its cargo hold.

marines, either to allow the crew to escape in emergencies or to allow divers to work outside the hull. The difference here, though, is that the air pressure inside the submarine is always lower than that of the water outside. Hence, if exit were attempted simply by opening a hatch, the vessel would be rapidly flooded.

An air lock allows the departing diver to seal the first hatch behind him, thus rendering the submarine safe, and then to open the valves on the outer door to let the sea water in. When the lock is filled with water, he can open the outer door and leave the vessel.

On re-entry, he shuts the outer door, blows out the sea water with compressed air, and closes the outer valves. Then he equalizes pressure with that inside the submarine at a speed necessary to prevent DECOMPRESSION SICKNESS, and enters the main hull.

See also: Air; Pressure; Space shuttle; Space vehicle; Submarine; Vacuum; Valve, mechanical.

Airplane

All heavier-than-air craft from a glider to a jet airliner rely on the application of mechanical energy to the air around to give an upward thrust, maintaining the craft in the air against gravitational forces.

This principle is the same for autogiros, helicopters, V/STOL airplanes, and anything that might be described as aerodynamic as opposed to airships or balloons, which derive lift by being lighter than the air they displace.

The relationship between lift and *drag* (a frictional force, for the most part) is expressed as a ratio known as the L/D ratio. For gliders this is very high, whereas supersonic jets, for instance, have low L/D ratios.

To maintain a heavier-than-air craft aloft requires a continuous input of energy – some means of maintaining the forward motion against wind resistance. Engine-driven propellers, jets or rockets supply the necessary thrust for this and for the aircraft to take off from the ground.

Typical layout

Basically, an airplane has a cigar-shaped fuselage for carrying crew, freight or passengers, on which is mounted a wing somewhere near the middle and a tailplane at the trailing end with a vertical tail fin. Added to this will be one or more engines mounted almost anywhere, ranging from inside the fuselage itself to the very tips of the wings.

With this layout, lift will usually be derived entirely from the wings and so the center of lift of the wings will normally correspond to the center of gravity of the aircraft.

Usually the main wing will not form a continuous horizontal line, but will be divided in the middle and raised toward the outside by a small amount relative to the center to give what is known as *dihedral*. Without this there would be nothing to keep the main axis of the wing horizontal during normal flight. As it is, dihedral results in greater lift from the lower wing when the aircraft tilts, thus producing a tendency to restore the wing to the horizontal mode.

The actual lift produced by a wing will vary with the speed of the plane. The faster it goes the more lift will be produced; this is why airplanes have to attain a considerable speed on the ground before they acquire enough lift for take off.

At the same time higher speeds involve more wind resistance – more drag – so jets and other high-speed aircraft have thin wings to reduce drag. If a plane slows down to below what is known as *stalling speed*, it literally falls out of the sky, the lift being insufficient to keep it flying. With thin wings the

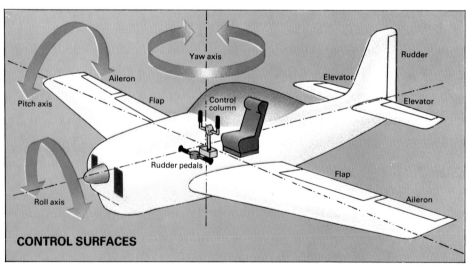

CONTROL SURFACES

Left: An airplane usually has three sets of control surfaces, which tilt it about three axes. The ailerons, which are moved by the control column, cause it to roll. The elevators, worked by moving the column forward or back, cause it to pitch. The rudder, worked by pedals, makes it yaw or swivel. A normal banked turn is made by simultaneously yawing and banking the aircraft.

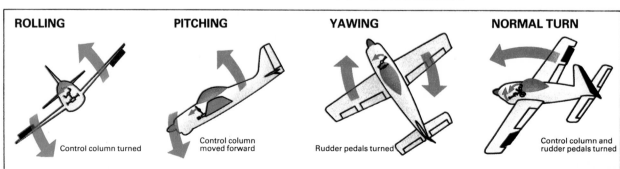

stalling speed tends to be higher than with thick wings, so jet aircraft require higher take-off and landing speeds.

It would be difficult to control a plane if these factors could not be varied. Jet aircraft would need enormously long runways because of their high minimum speeds, while if these factors were taken care of through thicker wings, their maximum speeds – one of the benefits of jets – would be severely cut.

A device known as the *flap* has therefore been developed to modify the wing section so that lift can be changed by the pilot. Part of the trailing edge of the wing, and sometimes part of the leading edge as well, is hinged downward to exaggerate the airfoil section and give more lift at lower speeds. The hinge is often arranged to open a slot between wing and flap through which air can flow to reduce turbulence. Fully extended flaps considerably increase drag, slowing the aircraft. This effect can be increased on some airplanes by opening out transverse flaps in the tops of the wings or elsewhere called air brakes.

Once an aircraft is in the air, it has to be capable of moving in three ways: in *pitch* – up and down; in *yaw* – side-to-side; and in *roll*.

Pitch is controlled by hinged surfaces on the trailing edge of the tailplane known as *elevators*. Moving these upward curves the tailplane into an inverted airfoil section, resulting in downward pressure on the tailplane and hence a tendency for the aircraft to adopt a nose-up or climbing attitude. Turning the elevators downward has the opposite effect.

Yaw is controlled by a flap on the tail fin known as the rudder. If the rudder alone is used the aircraft slews sideway, but this way of turning is inexact and badly controlled. There is no counteracting horizontal force to prevent the aircraft continuing to turn regardless of the pilot's wishes. Additionally, the horizontal centrifugal forces would tend to throw passengers and crew toward the outside of the turn.

By moving the *ailerons*, control surfaces on the outer wings, the aircraft can be made to bank or roll inward at the same time as the rudder turns it, so that the aircraft tilts toward the center of the turn like a bicycle. This is a more stable and comfortable way of turning.

In early aircraft the control surfaces – ailerons, elevators and rudder – were moved by the unaided exertion of the pilot through control wires. With today's high-speed aircraft, the forces on the control surfaces are much too great for this, and so they are now generally moved by hydraulic cylinders, operated by the pilot through servomechanisms. The arrangement works in a similar way to the power steering on a large car. This power assistance makes the controls of a modern aircraft very light, yet they are set to resist the pilot's action just enough to give an indication that the surfaces are responding properly.

To move the elevators, the pilot moves the column backward and forward and moves the ailerons by turning the control column. The rudder is

Below: The Rockwell B–1 bomber is a formidable combination of advanced design and complex avionics. A swing-wing, or variable geometry airplane, the wings rotate forward for greater stability at low speeds but sweep back for improved performance at high speeds and altitudes. Smooth lines and defensive avionics insure a low radar profile.

activated by two pedals, leaving the hands free to operate the other control surfaces at the same time for banked turns.

Variations in shape

Though the layout of conventional aircraft should remain the same for many years to come, there are now many other types made for specific purposes. Chief among these is the supersonic aircraft which has wings of a delta shape to reduce drag to a minimum and avoid problems with the shock wave caused by supersonic flight. Frequently such aircraft have no tailplane. The ailerons duplicate as elevators, and are known as *elevons*.

Supersonic aircraft invariably present a compromise in design because their shape differs from that of subsonic types, yet they have to fly subsonic as well. Inevitably, the result is an aircraft that is inefficient both subsonically and supersonically. To get around this problem, the swing wing concept has emerged. For subsonic flight, the wings stick out straight from the fuselage to produce adequate lift, but for supersonic flight they are swept back to form a delta shape. The mechanical problems of hinging a wing for this purpose are considerable, but several types are now flying.

Another aircraft type developed for a specific purpose is the VTOL (vertical take-off and landing) aircraft. Strictly speaking the helicopter, deriving lift from an overhead rotor, comes into this category, but normally it implies a conventional aircraft that has some additional system for getting it off the ground vertically.

The simplest VTOL aircraft incorporate secondary downward pointing jet engines that provide lift but contribute nothing to forward motion, this being achieved with horizontally mounted engines.

Others, such as the British Aerospace Harrier (also developed for the U.S. Navy as the AV8), deflect the normally horizontal jet exhaust downward to provide lift. The Bell and Boeing Helicopter Company has developed a successful aircraft – a tilt-rotor – in which the engines, driving large propellers, rotate from the horizontal to the vertical. The arrangement gives orthodox forward flight, the vertical movement and hover of a helicopter and a full range of thrust in between.

None of these arrangements excels in terms of efficiency because so much energy has to be dissipated in merely lifting the aircraft's dead weight, but they have good prospects for aircraft that can operate without airfields or can climb straight up to restrict the noise around airports. The armed forces find VTOL an attractive proposition because of the proven inherent flexibility of such aircraft – essential, for example, aboard aircraft carriers and in jungle warfare.

A compromise type, STOL (short take-off and

BOEING 767 200

Cutaway view of a Boeing 767 medium range airliner, which first entered service in 1982.

landing) offers similar, though more restricted advantages at lower cost. So far, most STOL types have been light aircraft with large flaps and other special control surfaces to give high lift at low speeds. Larger types have been developed for international passenger transportation, and these again offer a partial answer to the noise problem around large international airports.

Construction

The construction of all aircraft from simple glider to swing wing supersonic craft has to be carried out with one principal aim in view: to reduce weight as much as possible. Primitive types at the turn of the century adopted a wooden or steel tubular frame covered with canvas or similar material to provide

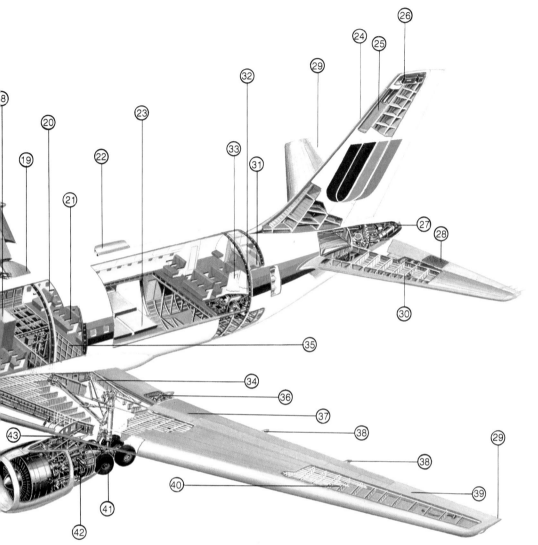

1 Radar dish
2 Radome
3 Captain
4 1st officer
5 Engineer
6 Engineer's panel
7 Jump seat
8 Entry doors (port and starboard)
9 Forward toilet
10 1st class cabin (18 seats)
11 Forward freight door
12 Electronics bay
13 Air conditioning riser ducts
14 Leading edge slat (extended)
15 Vent surge tank
16 Integral fuel tank (starboard)
17 Spoiler (deployed)
18 Toilets
19 Inboard double slotted flap
20 Rear spar fuselage frame
21 193 tourist seats
22 Open cargo door (rear)
23 10 cargo containers in rear freight hold
24 HF antenna
25 TV antenna
26 Tail VOR antennas
27 Auxiliary power unit (APU)
28 Honeycomb construction
29 Static dischargers
30 Tail logo light
31 Rear galley
32 Rear toilet
33 Pressurization unit
34 Undercarriage mounting beam
35 Wheel bay
36 Hinge link fairing
37 Inner aileron
38 Flap hinge fairings
39 Outer aileron
40 Stringers
41 Main undercarriage
42 Pratt and Whitney JT9D-7R4D
43 Engine mounting pylon
44 Slat drive motor
45 Air conditioning distribution ducts/manifolds
46 Landing and taxiing lights
47 Cargo containers
48 Electronics cooling plant
49 Nosewheels
50 Nosewheel bay
51 Glideslope antennas

the required aerodynamic surface. Such construction methods are still used for some simple light aircraft, though the canvas may also be replaced by glass fiber materials or aluminum sheet.

But for faster high-powered craft, where high dynamic forces are involved, such constructional practice would be unsuitable. Most larger aircraft use a reinforced *monocoque* construction, in which the outer shell takes a lot of the stress but is backed up by a suitable frame of light alloy. The shell is sometimes made of solid light alloy but nowadays tends to be a sandwich of two thin layers glued to a metal honeycomb mesh to give high stiffness with low weight. The aim is to produce a material akin to corrugated cardboard in cross section.

For supersonic aircraft, where the stress problem becomes even more acute, wings and other components have to be made by machining outer skin and frame together from solid pieces of alloy. Though giving the strength and heat resistance that are necessary, this method is very expensive and contributed considerably to the high cost of the Franco-British Concorde. It seems likely that it will be reserved strictly for military types in future. Both commercial and military aircraft now make considerable use of composite materials such as carbon fiber, which is lighter than most metals, with no known sacrifices of strength or durability.

See also: Aerodynamics; Aero engine; Aerospace industry; Aircraft; Airport; Aviation; Avionics; Inertial guidance; Jet engine and gas turbine.

Airport

Air travel is among the safest and most popular means of transport. In the U.S. for example, the number of passenger miles flown annually on scheduled domestic and local routes is measured in hundreds of thousands of millions.

Surprisingly, however, in all but a few instances, passengers board the intended plane at the expected location and take off and land on schedule. Such an outstanding success rate is the result of meticulous organization, and careful planning aided by the latest in high technology.

It was dificult in the early days of the airplane to envisage the growth potential of civil aviation and the complexity of air services and airports. Today, the spread of cities and the greater importance of air travel means that airports have to be planned to meet a careful balance between aviation and environmental needs.

A major airport requires a good highway and rail links with the city center. Passengers should be able to park their cars within a short walk of the terminal in which their airliner is docked. They do not want to have to park a long, confusing walk away, struggling with baggage through rain and traffic.

In between the car and the airliner, the airport,

airlines and control authorities, like immigration and customs, must provide the embarking passenger with, in order: ticket and check-in counters, passport checkpoints for international flights, concourses with lounge and general consumer services such as duty-free shops and a pier connecting the terminal with the door of the aircraft. The disembarking passenger wants to get out of the airliner as quickly as possible and either leave the airport or get to another berth to catch a connecting flight. If he is catching a connecting flight he wants to get to the appropriate berth – though it might be some distance away – without a long walk and without bothering about his baggage. All this has to be accomplished without mixing the inward and outward bound passengers.

Passengers who choose to go to and from the airport by rail have similar requirements. Ideally, their train should serve all the terminals of the airport without making passengers change. Another track should be used for automated shuttle services between all the berths.

To these passengers' requirements the airport designer must add those of the airlines. An airport like O'Hare Chicago employs about 80,000 people whose jobs include dealing with passengers and their baggage, servicing and refueling aircraft, air traffic control and so on. Nearly as many workers

Left: An aerial view of Schiphol airport in Holland. Arrivals to and departures from the airport itself are centered around the car parks and railway terminus (mostly underground here) to the right of the picture. The main airport building with its customer services and flight facilities is in the middle, and from this the long arms of the flight terminals themselves stretch out to the airplanes clustered around them on the ramp. Taxiways are designated by a white or yellow unbroken line down the middle and lead out to the runways. All airports are designed to similar specifications so that aircrews are not forced to adjust to differing national practices.

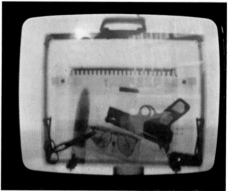

Left and above: International terrorism and air piracy have increased the need for airport security. Most departure gates now have X-ray equipment.

may go into and out of an airport each day as passengers. They want car parks and offices, and separate access for service vehicles to the airliners.

The aircraft themselves make great demands on space. Runways 2 miles (3.7 km) long and 150 ft (45 m) wide are required for modern commercial jets. There should be at least two runways, each aligned with the prevailing wind and with turn-offs and taxiways for the least taxiing time to and from the terminal building.

A modern airliner berth requires a terminal frontage of at least 100 yds (90 m). During rush hours at big airports there may be as many as 50 airliners in dock. This represents a frontage of some 3 miles (5 km). If each airliner has 350 seats it may generate a hundred cars; half a dozen airliners a day may dock in the berth and so parking for 600 cars has to be found near each berth.

The aircraft also need parking and maintenance space. Planes these days are designed for on-condition or on-wing maintenance, in which replacements for faulty units are simply fitted while the plane is parked.

Airliners have to be turned around as quickly as possible between flights to reduce costly time spent on the ground, when they are not actively earning money. The time between flights may be as little as 20 minutes, during which passengers have to be disembarked, the aircraft refueled, checked, cleaned and reprovisioned and the next group of passengers embarked.

Landings

The airliner approaches to land by ILS (Instrument Landing System). ILS equipment on the ground provides approaching airliners with heading (directional) and glidepath information. Aircraft normally join the center line (align themselves with the runway) 5 to 6 miles (8 to 10 km) from the runway

and follow the guidance beams until the aircraft has landed. The procedures are becoming increasingly automatic and many of the latest aircraft can carry out the complete approach and landing without any manual pilot control at all. This does require airport landing aids of the most up-to-date type.

ILS was originally designed for use in bad weather, but is now regularly used at major airports to keep traffic flowing.

RADAR is a valuable partner for ILS. Surveillance radar normally covers several hundred square miles of airspace around each airport. An incoming airliner is seen as a blip on the radar screen, which

Above: Firefighters at large airports use sophisticated equipment and train frequently to respond rapidly and effectively in the event of an emergency.

is used by the air traffic controller to steer the pilot on to the ILS beam.

Less busy airports use VOR (VHF Omnidirectional Range) beacons, which are also used as en route radio beacons. As an approach aid VOR is less satisfactory than ILS because it gives heading guidance only.

Visual landing aids are still important. The visual approach slope indicator, or VASI, which operates day and night, is not a substitute for ILS, being an airfield-in-sight aid. Bars of red and white lights on either side of the runway are angled to show the pilot all red lights when he is below the glidepath, red and white lights when he is on the correct glidepath, and all white when he is too high. These lights are on either side of the touchdown point of the runway.

The approach to the runway is indicated by Calvert approach lighting with a white center line crossed by five white bars, getting narrower as the runway approaches.

The runway itself has white center line lights and bars to mark the touchdown area. At the end of the runway, the center line becomes all red. The edges of the runway are marked with white lights. Taxiways have green center line lighting, with blue lights along the edges.

The lights set into the runway are carefully designed to withstand the 300 tons exerted by a landing aircraft, and yet present no obstacle. The light from a 200 W tungsten-halogen bulb shines through an aperture no more than 0.5 in. (13 mm) above the runway.

Runways have to be kept clear of obstacles – stones, parts of aircraft, and so on which can easily burst a tire. To insure this does not happen, vacuum cleaners and sweepers are used 24 hours a day. Snow clearance can be such a problem that plow blades, brushes and blowers are required.

Without doubt the airport's least used equipment is its fire, crash and rescue vehicles. The introduction of larger aircraft has required big increases in the quantities of fire-extinguishing materials, such as foam, that can be used. The trend is toward a knock-out punch – a large quantity of fire-damping material applied in one minute so that the passengers and crew can be disembarked as quickly and as safely as possible.

A fleet of Quick Dash Trucks carrying cutting devices, breathing apparatus, ladders, axes and other emergency rescue equipment is on constant alert in the event of an accident.

More commonly seen on the ground are aircraft tugs capable of pulling the heaviest aircraft. Also fuel tankers, which carry up to 24,000 gal (90,000 liters). A Boeing 747 has twice this capacity, so large airports use hydrants linked by underground piping to a fuel farm storage center. With this system, flow rates of thousands of gallons per minute are possible.

Above: Cargo-only Boeing 747. These aircraft are specifically designed for commercial freight loads, and have articulating nose cones.

Cargo handling

The airport provides the space, and the airline supplies the equipment, for cargo landing. The standard international pallets and containers are today common to the biggest and smallest airports. The transfer between aircraft hold and surface vehicle is dealt with by equipment ranging from the simple roller-slide or forklift truck to the more complex automatic power conveyers.

The scissor-lift platform lends itself well to big and heavy loads and also high holds, and is standard equipment – truck or trailer mounted – wherever cargo has to be offered up to aircraft of different hold heights. Aircraft victualing containers, for example, are frequently scissor-lifted to the aircraft galley door.

See also: Aerospace industry; Airplane; Air traffic control; Aviation; Baggage handling; Helicopter; Radar; Radio; Security system.

Airship

An airplane obtains its lift from its speed through the air and the AIRFOIL wing shape, whereas an airship or *dirigible* (meaning it can be steered or directed) uses a gas which is lighter than air. The motion is provided by motor-driven propellers.

The gas in the gasbag is considerably lighter than the air it displaces, thus making the airship as a whole slightly lighter than its own volume of air. It therefore rises until it has reached a height where the air is thinner, and so light enough to balance the weight of the airship.

This lift has to be controlled to make an airship workable. Early airships used to do this by releasing gas and replacing it with air, a wasteful method that caused gradual reduction of lift as more and more gas was lost. This loss could be compensated for by carrying water ballast, which could be released to lighten the airship. Later airships replaced the system with *ballonets*, collapsible air bags inside the gasbag but connected to the outside air. By varying the amount of air in the ballonets with pumps, the volume of the gas in the rest of the bag can be changed. There are usually two ballonets, to the forward and rear of the gasbag, so that the balance of the ship can be adjusted.

The tailfins operate just like those on an aircraft,

Below: A Goodyear blimp with a message for New York City. Airship design is once again emerging as a possibly cheaper alternative to conventional aircraft using increasingly costly fuels.

RIGID AIRSHIP

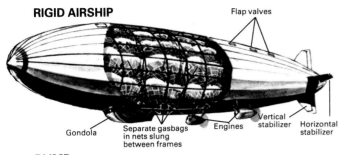

Flap valves

Gondola
Separate gasbags in nets slung between frames
Engines
Vertical stabilizer
Horizontal stabilizer

BLIMP

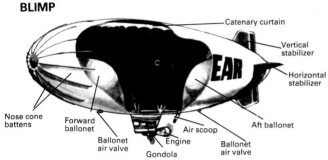

Catenary curtain

Vertical stabilizer

Horizontal stabilizer

Aft ballonet

Nose cone battens
Forward ballonet
Ballonet air valve
Engine
Air scoop
Gondola
Ballonet air valve

Above: Rigid airship and blimp. Early rigids had gasbags supported by nets and filled with hydrogen that was vented out of flap valves to let the airship descend. Blimps are filled with costly helium and contain air ballonets into which air can be pumped, thereby compressing the helium and making it heavier which in turn lowers the blimp.

Right: Inflating a blimp. The flexible envelope of the airship is laid out and filled with helium. Ballast weights attached to the blimp prevent it becoming airborne. Finally, passenger gondola and motors are attached prior to flight.

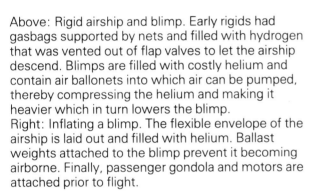

and are the control surfaces by which the ship is steered. Conventional elevators are used to change the altitude of the craft when it is moving; the change of atmospheric pressure with altitude is compensated for automatically by varying the amount of air in the ballonets.

The lightest gas is hydrogen, which is fairly inexpensive to manufacture. However its extreme flammability has resulted in the much more costly, slightly less effective, but completely safe helium being used in all modern airships. Helium is found in small amounts with natural gas in the U.S. but is otherwise very expensive to produce.

Types of airship

There are, or have been, three categories of airship, *rigid*, *semirigid* and *nonrigid*. The rigid types consisted of a light metal framework containing several gasbags slung inside under nets, and with a separate outer cover. The German Zeppelins and most airships of the 1920s and 1930s were of this type. The metals used were aluminum alloys, the outer skin was cotton, and the gasbags were cotton

lined with goldbeater's skin, a thin membrane taken from the intestines of cows.

The other types, semirigid and nonrigid, are known together as pressure airships since their shape is maintained mostly by the internal pressure. The semirigid types had a metal keel along the length of the envelope.

The type most commonly seen today is the nonrigid or *blimp*, which has no internal framework. Modern airships are made in this way of a synthetic fiber, Dacron, coated with neoprene, a synthetic rubber. Aluminum paint on the outside reflects the Sun's light and heat, reducing the extent to which the interior is heated. Battens reinforce the nose to prevent the wind pressure from flattening it when the craft is moving.

Development

In the beginning it was France that led the way. After the invention of the balloon in 1783, ways were sought of making it independent of the direction of the wind. The problem was to produce a suitable light yet powerful means of propulsion, and it was French innovator Henri Giffard who first produced a 3 hp engine that weighed about 350 lb (160 kg). His 75,000 cu ft (2124 m³) hydrogen-filled craft ascended from the Hippodrome in Paris in 1852, and flew at 5-6 mph (9 km/h) over the city.

Germany came into the picture in 1895 with the

Above: The cockpit of a modern blimp looks more like a conventional airplane flight deck than the ship's bridge early airships looked like.

Below: 7-passenger gondola of Skyship 500.

1 Radar compartment
2 Instrument panel
3 Kevlar/glass fiber body
4 Gondola support rigging
5 Gas envelope inspection dome

6 Ballonet control valves
7 Duct to ballonet
8 Cockpit
9 Access to gas envelope
10 Bulkhead
11 Electrics panel
12 Engines

13 Rudder cables
14 Water ballast tank
15 Ducted propeller can be rotated so that thrust can be directed up, down or for forward flight
16 Fuel tank

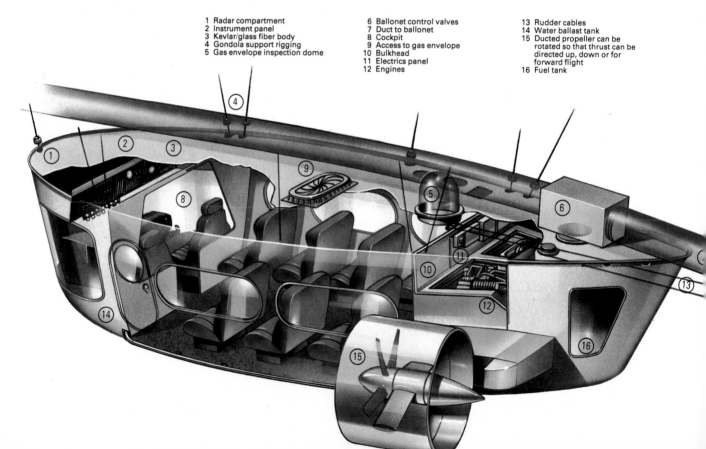

first rigid airship, built by David Schwarz. It was braced internally by a system of steel wires. Five years later, Count Zeppelin carried his idea further in his much bigger airship, built at Friedrichshafen. This had an aluminum frame consisting of 16 hoops connected and kept rigid by diagonal and longitudinal wire stays. The design proved a success and although one was lost, more than 20 airships of the same type were built.

In contrast, the British had given only spasmodic attention to the development of the airship. Consequently, at the Battle of Jutland, the British fleet had no airborne observers whereas the German fleet had the help of 29 airships. Soon the Zeppelins were making raids on English targets. The Royal Navy reacted quickly. They arranged for the construction of some small, nonrigid airships, which proved excellent at detecting and attacking enemy submarines. The British finished the war in 1918 with a fleet of 103; Germany had 68 rigids.

A fresh move was made by the British in 1918 through the purchase from Italy of a semirigid airship. This gave rise to a class of semirigids in the next few years. In the same period, the U.S. made an arrangement with the Zeppelin company out of which came the ZR1, called the Shenandoah, which used helium instead of hydrogen. After 57 flights she was lost in a thunderstorm. The U.S. persisted in development work and, apart from building the Akron and the Macon, both of 6 million cu ft (17,000 m³) capacity, invented a metal skin for small airships.

The heyday of the giant rigid airship was in the late 20s and 30s. The U.S. decided to use only helium in its airships; she also banned its export. This meant that the large British and German craft had to rely upon hydrogen. The flammability of the gas and the lack of maneuverability of the ships often had appalling consequences. Many of the largest airships met with disaster, notably the British R101 in 1930, the American Akron and Macon in 1933 and 1935, and the Zeppelin Hindenburg in 1937.

The heavy loss of life in these crashes swung opinion against the use of airships, and they were no longer used for carrying passengers. But later, during World War II, the U.S. used large numbers of nonrigid airships without a single loss for sea patroling. Their ability to operate for long periods of time at low speed and low altitude made them invaluable for minesweeping and escorting convoys.

Postwar revival

In recent years, advances in aeronautical engineering and technology have led to a resurgence of interest in airships, especially of the nonrigid kind, as a safe means of transport for passengers and particularly cargoes. New materials such as carbon fibers and titanium alloys, polyamide-based syn-

Above: One of many designs for possible future airships. The spherical body rotates in order to improve aerodynamic efficiency.

thetic fabrics, Mylar and Neoprene-coated Dacron, together with computer aided trim and ballast controls, gas turbine, diesel and even nuclear power plants have revolutionized the potential of airships, or *aerostats* to give them their generic name. Even during the 1950s, the possibility of equipping military airships with some form of nuclear propulsion was examined, but never taken up, although the U.S. Navy did order 4 early-warning radar airships from Goodyear which were eventually scrapped in 1962.

Meanwhile the trend toward airships has continued to gain momentum, not least through the efforts of Goodyear who have alone produced over 300 dirigibles for commercial purposes in recent years. By the mid 1980s these craft were being used for aerial advertising and as vibration-free television camera platforms for sporting events, aerial and geological surveying and, especially in Canada and Russia, for lumber work.

Already the way is being paved for cargo airships to operate away from existing airplane freight routes, though it may be some time before the stately, unhurried airship can compete realistically with conventional high-speed, wide-bodied aircraft for long-haul passenger transport which is becoming increasingly cost-efficient with the introduction of even less voracious power units.

See also: Aerial photography; Aerodynamics; Air cushion vehicle; Aviation; Balloon; Fiber, synthetic; Gas laws; Hydrogen; Navigation.

Liftoff for superballoons

After almost 50 years, the airship is making a comeback with a new range of super balloons that make use of the latest available technology.

The leader in the new airship stakes is the British built Skyship 500 which uses in its construction advanced materials and new techniques never before applied in such a way.

The Skyship 500 has been built and developed in the enormous hangar that once house the ill-fated R101 airship. However, the 500 at just 164 ft (50 m) long is little more than a fifth the length of the R101. Another important difference is that the 500 is a nonrigid structure.

The other key improvement is that unlike the R101 and the Hindenburg, the 500 is filled with inert helium instead of highly flammable hydrogen – the gas which eventually caused the destruction of many of the early breed of airships.

The 500's design has made use of the most advanced materials in its construction. The balloon's envelope, for example, is made from a new French-built polyester material; the gondola (the cabin slung under the balloon) is made from Kevlar; the tailfin and bulkheads are made from a honeycomb sandwich of the materials used in high-speed boats.

One of the most significant features of the Skyship 500 is its power plant. The airship is powered by two Porsche 930 six-cylinder automobile engines which drive propulsors mounted on either side of the gondola and which can operate continu-

Above: One of the Goodyear helium filled blimps. Right: The Airship Industries Skyship 500 over London – identical to the aircraft used by British Caledonian Airways to provide tourists with a bird's eye view of the city. Powered by two Porsche 930/10 air-cooled six-cylinder units delivering 120 bhp at a cruising speed of 60 knots (111 km/h). Top right: The Cyclo-Crane is a cross between a balloon and an airplane.

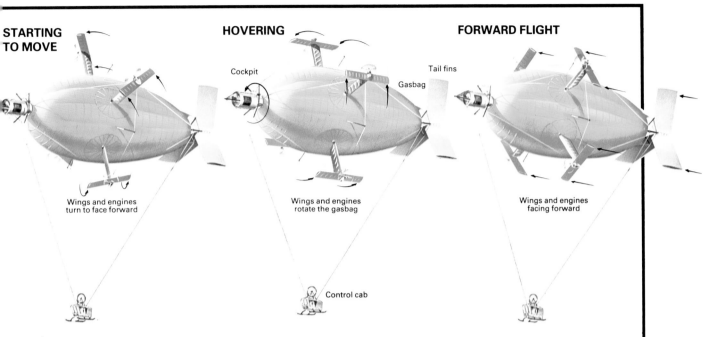

STARTING TO MOVE

Wings and engines turn to face forward

HOVERING

Cockpit

Wings and engines rotate the gasbag

Control cab

FORWARD FLIGHT

Tail fins

Gasbag

Wings and engines facing forward

ously for up to 30 hours. The propulsors, five-bladed fans mounted within ducts, can be rotated to provide vectored thrust upward, downward or straight forward.

The 500 and a slightly larger version, the 600 – already in production – are attracting considerable interest from governments who want to use the airships for coastal patrols.

With a top speed of 62 knots (114 km/h), the Skyship can overtake any ship, descend to talk to its captain by bullhorn and even lower a rubber dinghy, if necessary, to board the vessel. The Skyship could also be used for carrying long-range radar equipment. Airship Industries, Skyship's manufacturers, are also planning a Skyship 5000 – a much bigger airship which is expected to carry 200 passengers from London to Paris in two-and-a-half hours.

Britain is not the only country with plans to revive airships – other projects are being pursued in North America, one in Canada and the others in the U.S.

Oregon-based Aerolift Inc. has developed a prototype of the Cyclo-Crane which is a cross between a balloon and a conventional aircraft. The Cyclo-Crane is a hybrid aircraft which uses aerostatic lift from a helium-filled balloon to support all of its structural weight plus half the weight of the load it has to carry. The rest of the necessary lift and thrust for forward movement and control comes from a system of airfoils that rotate when the Cyclo-Crane is hovering and move to become aligned with the direction of flight when the Cyclo-Crane reaches its maximum forward (or backward) speed.

The Cyclo-Crane is designed to revolve at 16 rpm when it is loading or unloading. When it picks up speed in forward flight, the rotation slows down to compensate for the increasing velocity of the wings in relation to the air.

Designers of the Cyclo-Crane believe they have solved the age-old problem of the maneuvering of airships. The addition of the rotating wings will, they believe, make the Cyclo-Crane as easy to control as a helicopter though it will operate with far greater economy – between a quarter and half the cost of using a helicopter.

The concept of the Cyclo-Crane is particularly interesting to the Canadians because of its potential in forestry work in transporting felled trees from inaccessible areas.

Its manufacturers also believe that the Cyclo-Crane could be used as a passenger carrier on domestic flights particularly on commuter routes in the US – charging fares which would only be a quarter of those charged by scheduled airlines at the moment. A 50-ton Cyclo-Crane could carry about 550 people in a transport pod slung beneath the craft. The Cyclo-Crane would carry the incoming transport pod to a berth, release the pod and reconnect to an outgoing pod already full of passengers.

Despite the obvious advances that have been made in design, people are still very suspicious of airships through memories of the Hindenburg and R101 disasters. "It's ridiculous," said one of the men behind the Skyship 500: "You can't compare a modern airship with the R101 – it's like comparing a Boeing 747 with a 1918 Vickers Vimy."

Air traffic control

Air traffic control, ATC, is one of the crucial factors in air safety. It is a system for preventing collisions between aircraft in congested areas particularly in the neighborhood of airports where the air is full of aircraft of different sizes, traveling in various directions at various speeds and heights. ATC also keeps air traffic flowing smoothly.

On those parts of long-distance routes which are uncongested, the pilot uses the built-in navigational aids of the aircraft, and sometimes electronic aids on the ground, to navigate and avoid collisions by flying predetermined routes at specified heights. As soon as a flight approaches a much flown-over area, or nears an airport, it enters a control zone, where it is obliged to follow a specific course at a given speed and height prescribed by the air traffic controller.

The air traffic controller is the decision maker, who alone has complete information on all aircraft movements within the control zone. The controller exercises discretion on the minimum safe spacing between aircraft, both vertically and horizontally, and determines priority in take-off and landing within the framework of flight schedules.

The minimum information required by a controller is the current height and position of all aircraft under his or her control, the intentions of all aircraft under, or soon to be under control, and the identity of each aircraft. The controller gets this information from a *flight progress board* which informs on intention, identification, vertical position and timing, and from a *plan position radar* which gives the exact position and distance of all aircraft within the control zone.

The controller's work involves continuous updating of information as new situations develop and earlier ones pass from his or her control. Controllers receive advance information of traffic about to enter each control zone from adjacent zones and inform adjacent zones of traffic leaving each zone. They also monitor and control all traffic within a zone.

The controller communicates with the aircraft normally by VHF (very high frequency) radiotelephone with a range of up to 200 miles (300 km) when the aircraft is at high altitude, although the

range decreases as the aircraft descends. A *radio direction finder* (RDF) system is frequently employed with the VHF radio link to supply the compass bearing of any call received.

Wind speed and direction, visibility, cloud base, air temperature and barometric pressure data are fed to the controller from local sources and from meteorological centers. Runway visibility can now be accurately measured by electronic means. The days of having to estimate conditions are past.

Flight plans

With certain exceptions, each flight requires a *flight plan* which includes aircraft identification, airport of departure and destination, route plan, desired cruising level, departure time and elapsed time of the flight.

The data is transmitted, generally by land line or computer link rather than radio, to the Air Traffic Control center from airports within the controller's zone or from adjacent zones.

The information is always to a standard format, to minimize the risk of omission and to simplify its communication.

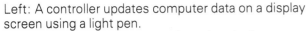

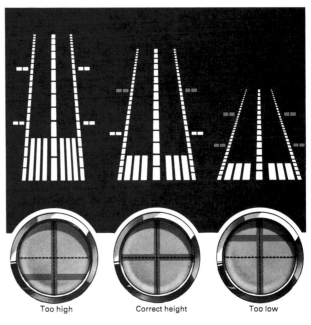

Too high   Correct height   Too low

Left: A controller updates computer data on a display screen using a light pen.
Above: Surface movement radar at London's Heathrow airport.
Right and above right: Runway approach lights, with Visual Approach Slope Indicator (VASI) lights each side. Each light has two narrow beams – one red, one white. If the airplane is too low, the pilot sees both sets of VASI lights as red, if too high, they appear white. For a correct alignment, red should be seen over white.

Radar control systems

The basic RADAR system gives a continuous plan, as seen from above, of all aircraft within radar range. The Plan Position Indicator (PPI) radar display shows an aircraft target as a bright spot with the range (distance) of the aircraft indicated by its distance from the center of the screen and its bearing by the angle to the center. An electronic means known as video mapping makes it possible permanently to superimpose fixed features such as defined airways on the screen. It is also possible to eliminate all

unwanted permanent radar echoes from stationary objects and display only those which are actually moving (moving target indicators).

In yet another refinement the radar echo from a particular aircraft can be tagged with its identity or other information as a code of letters and numbers. The identity tag of each aircraft slowly moves across the screen in synchronization with the movement of the aircraft.

PPI type radars are in three broad categories: long-range surveillance, airfield control and airfield surface movement. Long-range surveillance radars have typically up to 300 nautical miles (550 km) range from approximately two megawatts peak power. Airfield control radars operating at less power have typically 50 to 150 nautical miles (95 to 280 km) range. Airfield surface movement radars are designed for very high definition and range is

Above: A VOR/DME (VHF Omnidirectional Radio Range/Distance Measuring Equipment) array which provide aircraft with course data.

normally confined to runways, taxi ways and aprons of the immediate airfield. Modern surface movement radars have sufficient picture resolution to identify individual aircraft types.

These radars are all of the primary type, which obtain information from a reflection of the radar beam from the aircraft or other target, and

Below: ILS (Instrument Landing System) uses narrow beams to guide aircraft. The stacking beam marks where they line up, marker beams indicate distance, and localizer and glide path beams mark the correct line of approach. A clearance antenna wipes out unwanted parts of the beam.

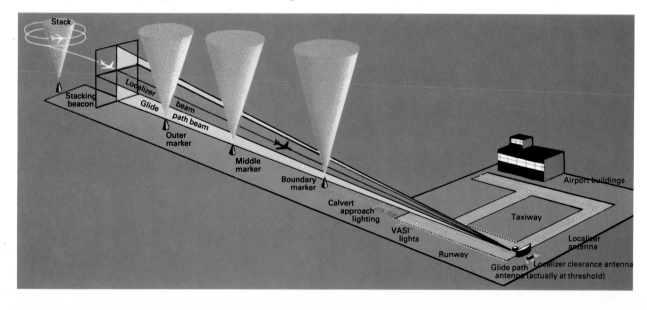

require no cooperation from the aircraft. Another important type of radar system is known as Secondary Surveillance Radar (SSR) in which equipment carried on the aircraft receives the transmitted ground signal and transmits a reply. The reply is entirely automatic and generally includes a coded message giving identity of the aircraft and present altitude, both of which can be integrated into the main PPI display and tagged to the appropriate aircraft on the display.

Instrument landing system

The controller normally controls aircraft up to the final approach to the airfield when the pilots can lock on to the Instrument Landing System (ILS). This system provides a fixed radio beam so that an aircraft can align itself with the runway and adopt the correct descent path. The equipment comprises two ground transmitters, one emitting a beam to guide the aircraft in *azimuth* or compass bearing, the other a beam to guide the aircraft in altitude. The beams are known respectively as the *localizer* and *glidepath*. Both beams are modulated with tones at audio frequency (at a pitch which enables them to be heard) which are used to activate instruments in the aircraft flight deck or indicate audibly to the pilot whether the plane is deviating to the left or right of the center line and above or below the glidepath.

Along the approach center line are three vertically transmitted fan-shaped beams known as the outer, middle, and inner *marker beacons*. Once brought to the position for final approach, the marker beacons indicate the distance to go, and the ILS system proper shows any deviation from the center line and glidepath. If the pilot keeps to the center line and glidepath the aircraft will be brought to the threshold of the runway at about 200 ft (60 m) altitude and can then complete the landing visually. The controller directs the aircraft to the appropriate runway exit.

Blind landing

Suitably equipped aircraft can use ground-based ILS (provided it is exceptionally accurate) combined with the autopilot and additional airborne electronic aids (principally highly accurate radar ALTIMETERS) to land in near zero visibility. The main complexity in such a system is the duplication and even triplication of airborne equipment to secure acceptable reliability.

Blind landing has been achieved thousands of times in commercial practice. The pilot monitors the landing throughout and can take manual control at any instant.

Modern aids

The electronic computer plays a central role in ATC. It processes and stores information and supplies data to individual controllers in a large

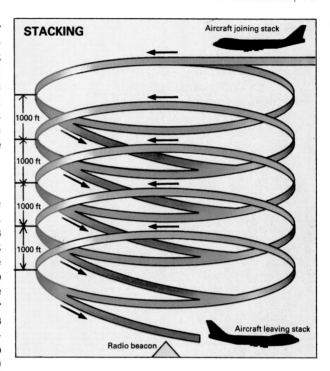

Above: When an airport is too busy for incoming aircraft to land immediately, they have to circle in stacks until a runway is free. A vertical distance of 1000 ft (305 m) separates levels.

complex. The computer's main function is to reduce what would otherwise be a very demanding workload on controllers so that they can concentrate on supervision of aircraft movements and the all-important decision making.

The Eurocontrol Maastricht Automatic Data Processing system (MADAP), which became fully operational in 1975, is a good example of an ATC system because it is multinational in the equipment used, the ATC officers who work in it, the countries that support it and the many aircraft which fly through its area of operation.

MADAP controls the upper air space of a region of Europe covering Belgium, Luxemburg, parts of The Netherlands and the northern part of the Federal Republic of Germany. Its design incorporates all the features outlined above with the exception of ILS and other ground aids which do not apply to upper air space.

The ATC center receives data from four radar centers and a continuous stream of flight data from airports and adjoining areas. All inputs, including radar data, are then processed through high-power computers to provide controllers with the information they want as soon as it is needed. For example, incoming flight plans are held in computer store until the aircraft concerned enters the area.

See also: **Airport; Aviation; Navigation; Radar.**

Alcohol

Alcohol is most familiar as an ingredient of alcoholic drinks, but drinkable alcohol is only one of many different kinds.

Drinking alcohol is properly known as *ethyl' alcohol* or *ethanol* and it can be fatal in large doses. Small amounts of other alcohols can cause brain damage and death.

Industrial alcohol is used as a solvent and in the manufacture of acetic acid, plastics such as polyethylene (Polythene), ether, chloroform, and the tetraethyl lead added to gasoline as an anti-knock compound – though this additive has been or is being banned in many countries, including the U.S., because it is poisonous. Industrial applications account for approximately one-third of total world production of alcohol the remaining two-thirds being used for drinking.

Methyl alcohol or *methanol* (wood alcohol, so called because it was originally made from the destructive *distillation* of wood) is used as a solvent, in the manufacture of formaldehyde and in anti-freeze. It is also used in *methylated spirit*, which is ethanol made undrinkable by adding about 9 per cent methanol and very small amounts of benzene, pyridine and dye which, by their taste, smell and color, considerably reduce the danger of accidental poisoning.

Ethanediol or *ethylene glycol* (sometimes referred to simply as *glycol*) is also used in antifreeze, to make various plastics and synthetic resins such as polyurethane, and many modern adhesives. *Glycerol* (also known as glycerine) is used to make other plastics, explosives (nitroglycerine), cosmetics, inks and antifreeze. It is a by-product in soap making.

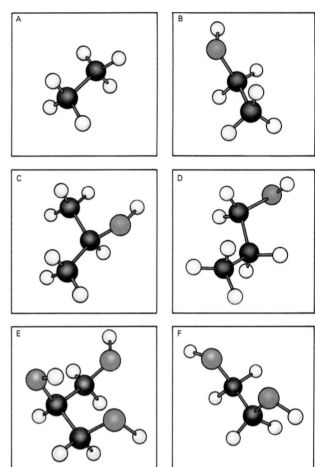

Above: Molecular models of A – ethane, B – ethanol, C – isopropanol, D – propanol, E – glycerol, F – ethylene glucol. The black spheres represent carbon atoms, red spheres, oxygen and white, hydrogen.

Structure of alcohols

When one or more of the hydrogen atoms in a hydrocarbon is replaced by the hydroxyl group, –OH, the result is an alcohol. Ethane, C_2H_6, for example, becomes ethanol, C_2H_5OH. Hence the names for alcohols: methanol, ethanol, propanol, butanol and so on, corresponding to the related hydrocarbon gases, methane, ethane, propane and butane. These alcohols, which contain a single hydroxyl group, range from volatile liquids to waxy solids.

Structurally, from propanol onward, the alcohols show *isomerism* – that is, there is more than one position where the –OH group can go, although the overall number of carbon, hydrogen and oxygen atoms remains the same. This structural difference can give molecules different characteristics, which means that they undergo different types of chemical reactions. For example, primary alcohols (where the –OH group is attached to the end of a carbon chain) can be oxidized to aldehydes and to carboxylic acids, while secondary alcohols are oxidized to ketones. In secondary alcohols, such as isopropyl alcohol or propan-2-ol, the hydroxyl group is attached to a carbon atom which is in the middle of a carbon chain.

Alcohols with more than one hydroxyl group are known as *polyols*. Both ethanediol and glycerol belong to this class.

Reactions of alcohols

Alcohols can be burned (for example, methylated spirit) to give carbon dioxide and water vapor. They react with both inorganic and organic acids to give esters. This is the equivalent of an inorganic reaction between an acid and an alkali to give a chemical salt. For example, hydrochloric acid reacts with caustic soda to give sodium chloride. Similarly, methanol will react with salicylic acid to give methyl salicylate, or oil of wintergreen as it is com-

Above: Distilling equipment in a typical Scottish distillery making malt whisky, which has to be distilled twice. Most alcohol production is, however, industrial rather than comestible.

monly known. Alcohols can be dehydrated (water can be removed from them) to give ethers or olefins (alkenes) depending on the reaction conditions.

Production of alcohols
Most of the ethyl alcohol for industrial purposes is produced by the hydration of ethylene using high temperature and a suitable CATALYST.

$$\begin{array}{ccccc} C_2H_4 & + & H_2O & \rightarrow & CH_3CH_2OH \\ \text{ethylene} & & \text{water} & & \text{ethanol} \end{array}$$

Methanol is made by the action of hydrogen on oxides of carbon using high pressure, moderately high temperature and a catalyst.

Ethanol, for drinking purposes, is made by the *fermentation* of sugars. Hexose sugars ($C_6H_{12}O_6$) are needed for the fermentation action in which yeast cells produce an ENZYME which splits the sugar into alcohol and carbon dioxide. This gas causes the

liquid to froth, which gives the process its name – fermentation from the Latin *fervere*, meaning to boil. The amount of alcohol produced will depend on the strain or type of yeast used and the temperature. Sometimes, in the fermentation of grapes in winemaking, the yeast used is that present naturally as a bloom on the skin of the grape. In most wine making, however, and in the brewing of beer, where barley is used as a source of starch and ultimately of sugar, the yeast is added.

Usually, starch in the form of barley, rice, potatoes or maize is hydrolyzed or broken down into a sugar, *maltose*, by the action of an organic catalyst which occurs naturally and is known as an enzyme. In brewing, the germination of the grain produces the enzyme. A sweet liquid or *wort* results and this is turned into glucose by another enzyme, *maltase*, which is found in yeast. The glucose is turned into alcohol by a third enzyme, *zymase*, also found in yeast. Dilute acid or alkali may be used instead of enzymes for converting starch to sugars.

See also: Beer and brewing; Bond, chemical; Chemistry; Distillation; Fermentation; Poison; Soap manufacture; Spirit; Winemaking; Yeast.

Algae

The algae are a varied group of primitive plants ranging in size from microscopic single cells to giant kelp, a seaweed which can sometimes reach a length of 600 ft (180 m).

In common with other plants, most algae contain the green pigment CHLOROPHYLL, but in addition to the green forms, algae may be colored blue-green, red, or brown. They possess no true roots, stems or leaves, and are characteristically soft and gelatinous. Some algae, however, such as diatoms, produce a hard skeleton containing silica, and others produce stony coral-like deposits.

In Japan, the delicate red seaweed *Porphyra* is commonly eaten, and is extensively cultivated. Another popular Japanese food is *kombu*: this is prepared from large brown seaweeds such as the *Laminaria*.

A potentially valuable project is the cultivation of small aquatic algae, such as *Chlorella*, for large-scale production of food. After harvesting the algae, a flourlike substance is obtained which may contain 50 per cent protein, or by varying the method of cultivation, high levels of fat. *Chlorella* is only 0.004 in. (0.1 mm) in diameter and, under favorable conditions, there may be millions of cells in each milliliter of culture medium. Pilot plants have produced yields of 100 lbs (45 kg) of dried *Chlorella* per acre each day, but so far, high production costs have rendered the process uneconomic.

Chlorella and other small algae are also used for sewage purification. Sunlight causes algae to release oxygen, which is used by bacteria in the sewage to break down solid and liquid wastes. This process is carried out in large, shallow lagoons, and needs a considerable amount of sunlight. Experiments have shown that the algae can be separated from the slurry, chemically treated, dried, and used as an animal-feed additive.

NASA has experimented with waste-recycling and oxygen-producing systems based on *Chlorella*. Such systems would be most useful during interplanetary travel, and could reduce the amount of bulky gas cylinders and purifying equipment carried. The algae feed on carbon dioxide and excreted waste, and give off oxygen for use inside the spacecraft.

Agar-agar is a jellylike material which is usually extracted from the red alga *Gelidium*. It is used as a

Above right: *Euglena,* magnified 950 times, one of the types of algae used to break down waste matter in the treatment of sewage.
Right: Giant Californian kelp beds are sprayed by boat with concentrated liquid fertilizer in an attempt to further boost the growth rates.

Top: Alginates are a major source of additive in the mass manufacture of many processed foods.
Above: Factory farmed on foreshore nets, species of Porphyra are the commonest types of seaweed cultivated in Japan. Rich in protein and vitamins A and C, the seaweed is turned into a noodlelike substance called Nori which is eaten in soups and stews, or can be boiled down and fried.

thickening agent in food, and in the laboratory as a culture medium for bacteria and fungi.

Extensive use is made of alginates in a variety of industries. Alginates are extracted from brown kelp such as *Macrocystis* or *Ascophyllum* and purified. Their thickening, gelling and film-forming properties make alginates important food additives.

They thicken ketchup and stabilize salad dressings and soft drinks against separation. Their gelling properties are used in dessert products, bakery fillings and restructured foods. The inclusion of alginates retards ice crystal formation (grittiness) and fat clumping in ice cream.

In the pharmaceutical industry, alginates facilitate tablet disintegration, are used in surgical dressings, *hemostats* (used to stem the flow of blood from a wound) and as active ingredients in some preparations for stomach disorders. Another major application is in the printing of textile fabrics. Alginates offer excellent evenness, fine line definition coupled with soft handling in the printing of cotton with reactive dyes and polyester with disperse dyes.

A rather different algal derivative, DIATOMACEOUS earth, or kieselguhr, which consists of the skeletal remains of fossil diatoms, is used as a filter medium, a filler compound for paints, an abrasive in metal polishes and toothpastes, and as a heat resisting lining for furnaces.

See also: Cell; Drug; Fabric printing; Food processing; Oxygen; Protein; Sewage treatment.

Aliphatic and aromatic compound

Aliphatic compounds are open-chain organic compounds which occur widely in products as diverse as gasoline, methane gas, butter, sugar and meat.

These compounds contain carbon combined with hydrogen or often oxygen and nitrogen, and sometimes other ELEMENTS may be present. They range from simple gases such as methane (CH_4) to very large and complex compounds such as PROTEINS, which in addition to containing the elements carbon, hydrogen, oxygen and nitrogen may also include sulfur and phosphorus.

Organic substances were orginally divided into

two main groups depending on whether they were related to the fats or to the aromatic oils (essential oils) and spices. The essential oils are found as the fragrances of plants and occur in flowers, fruit, leaves, stems and sometimes timber. The two main groups were known as aromatic and fatty or aliphatic (Greek *aleiphar* – fat).

Later, as the knowledge of organic compounds increased, a more exact system of classifying them into four main groups arose. These were aliphatic, alicyclic, aromatic (here, benzene derivatives) and heterocyclic compounds. Aliphatic compounds can be divided into groups of compounds with similar properties. Aliphatic compounds include esters, ethers, HYDROCARBONS, alcohols, aldehydes, KETONES, CARBOXYLIC ACIDS, AMINES, carbohydrates, AMINO ACIDS and proteins.

Below and right: A wide range of household products is based on many aliphatic compounds: 1 – wool (a type of protein known as keratin), 2 – butterscotch essence, 3 – linseed oil, 4 – red beans, 5 – methylated spirit, 6 – olive oil, 7 – carboxylic acid, acetic acid, 8 – acetone, 9 – the action of alkali on fatty acids used in soap manufacture, 10 – skin perfume, 11 – lighter fuel, 12 – butane gas, 13 – cheese (over 50% protein and fat), 14 – meat, 15 – melamine formaldehyde plastic, 16 – starch, 17 – sugar. All of these either contain aliphatic compounds, or else they rely on the action of them in a manufacturing process.

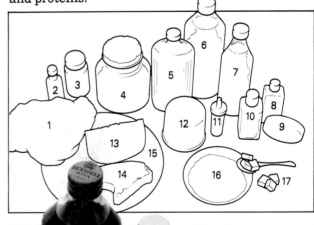

Aromatic compounds are an important group of substances in organic chemistry, all based on benzene, C_6H_6. The word aromatic is used because many of these compounds have a pleasant smell. This applies particularly to the essential oils which give plants their fragrances such as vanillin, oil of bitter almonds, and eugenol, which is found in clove oil. Common aromatic solvents such as toluene and xylene, and even benzene itself, also have agreeable odors which make them attractive to abusers.

Important sources of aromatic compounds include coal and crude oil. When coal is heated to around 1800° F (1000° C) without any air being present various volatile products are given off and the coal is converted to coke. Some of these products are naturally gaseous, such as coal gas (sometimes used for domestic gas supplies) and ammonia, but the rest condense on cooling and are collected. The condensed mixture includes crude benzole, crude tar and naphthalene and is a useful source of various aromatic compounds, including benzene, xylene, toluene and phenol.

Structure of benzene

The benzene molecule is composed of six carbon and six hydrogen atoms arranged in a hexagonal ring, an unusual shape which gives it useful chemical properties. This is because of the way the atoms are linked together.

Atoms of different substances have a different number of ELECTRONS orbiting around them, arranged in *shells* or layers. An atom with eight electrons in its outer shell is stable, and will not react with other atoms. The INERT GASES, such as argon, neon and xenon, which are totally non-reactive, have eight electrons in their outer shells.

Other, less stable atoms are constantly trying to reach this balanced state, and they do this by gaining or losing or mutually sharing electrons with other atoms to make up the number eight in their outer shells. In this way atoms may have from one to seven spare outer shell electrons. The number any atom has is known as its VALENCY number.

Carbon has a valency of four; hydrogen of one. So a substance such as acetylene, C_2H_2, does not have very stable molecules. Each carbon atom shares one electron with a hydrogen atom (a single bond), but there are still six electrons unaccounted for. These arrange themselves into pairs forming a flimsy triple bond between the two carbon atoms, which is easily broken if there are any other suitable atoms around with which they can combine. Molecules in this state are called unsaturated and are very reactive, which accounts for acetylene's readiness to burn; a most useful property.

Benzene, with its formula of C_6H_6, is unsaturated, and it seems that it ought to be unstable. In fact it is exceptionally stable; this puzzled chemists for years

Above: Metallurgical coke, used in metal smelting, is the source of many aromatic compounds, including toluene, benzene and xylene.

after its discovery by Michael Faraday in 1825. The reason was hit on in 1865 by Kekulé, who realized that the atoms are arranged in a hexagonal ring. He decided that the six carbon atoms must be joined by alternating single and double bonds, which he assumed oscillated rapidly from one position to the other. It is more complex than this.

One of the four valency electrons from each carbon atom is able to zoom round the molecule in either direction. In all six electrons orbit round the ring structure giving benzene a hybrid type of bonding which is neither double nor single, but something in between. Diagrammatically, however, it is often represented as alternating single and double bonds. It's also sometimes represented as a circle inside a hexagon.

Although the ring is stable, the hydrogen atoms on the corners can be detached and replaced by various *radicals* (groups of atoms) to form stable, useful compounds. The benzene ring acts as a kind of chassis to hold the radicals in place.

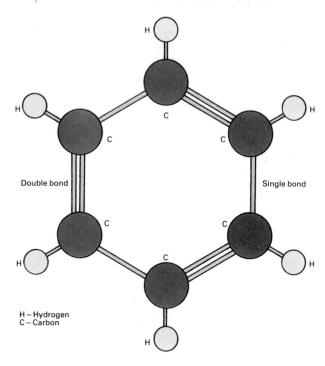

Double bond   Single bond

H – Hydrogen
C – Carbon

Above: Structure of the benzene ring. Its useful chemical properties are due to the complicated bonding between its carbon atoms.

Useful benzene derivatives

Most households contain numerous products made from aromatic compounds. There are disinfectants based on phenol, C_6H_6OH, better known as carbolic acid. Unlike phenol, which is very corrosive and therefore dangerous, its derivatives, the chlorophenolic products such as chloroxylenol and TCP, are harmless to the human body but still effective as antiseptics. Phenol is also used for making various phenol formaldehyde resins, the best known being the plastic Bakelite. The *cresols* which are methylated derivatives of phenol are widely used in the Lysol type of disinfectant. *Aminophenols* are important starting materials for many dyes, and they can undergo modifications to give two different but very useful compounds: phenacetin, the painkiller and dulcin, which is a sweetening agent. Polyhydric phenols contain more than one hydroxyl (−OH) group. The hormone adrenalin, used as a heart stimulant, is synthesized from one of these phenols, catechol. Other important members of the group are hydroquinone, which is a photographic developer, and resorcinol, which is the basis of the powerful antiseptic n-hexylresorcinol, the active constituent of Listerine.

When phenol is nitrated with nitric acid, it forms the bright yellow crystals of picric acid, which is sometimes used to relieve pain on bad burns. Picric acid is also used to make dyes and a high explosive known as lyddite.

Toluene, $C_6H_5CH_3$, is a liquid which closely resembles benzene, probably best known for its pale yellow, crystalline derivative trinitrotoluene, the explosive TNT. It is also the starting point for many aromatic compounds, among them the painkiller novocaine, the sweetener saccharine, and various dyes. Another aromatic solvent similar to toluene and benzene is xylene, $C_6H_4(CH_3)_2$. The synthetic fiber Terylene (Dacron) is made from xylene and ethylene. The xylene is converted to terephthalic acid, $C_6H_4(COOH)_2$, and the ethylene to the alcohol ethylene glycol. These products condense to form

Left: Modern agriculture relies extensively on the spraying of crops with insecticides and herbicides. The herbicide MCPA (methylchlorophenoxy-acetic acid) works selectively, normally attacking only broad leaved plants. Here it has killed the charlock (right side of the pole) by stimulating its growth so rapidly that the plant burnt itself up metabolically, leaving the cereal on the left to flourish.

the polymer fiber (polymers have long chainlike molecules from which their strength is derived).

Apart from Bakelite, a more recently discovered plastic is the light and strong polystyrene. Ethyl benzene is dehydrogenated (the hydrogen is removed) to give vinyl benzene, which is the basis of the links in the polystyrene chain.

Tropical diseases in particular have been controlled by the development of drugs containing the benzene ring. In 1944 a highly effective drug for malaria, paludrine, was synthesized. More powerful than quinine, it has the added benefit of not having quinine's unpleasant side effects, such as yellowing the skin. The discovery of another drug, salvarsan (arsphenamine), by Paul Ehrlich in 1909 was based on an interesting observation. He noticed that synthetic dyestuffs dyed only certain parts of animal cells and decided that the stain might perhaps be used selectively to kill bacteria. His aromatic arsenic compound was found to be effective against syphilis, though harmless against trypanosomes which cause sleeping sickness in humans, and for which it was intended to be used. Sulfanilamide, $NH_2.C_6H_4.SO_2NH_2$, had been first prepared in Austria in 1908, but not until the 1930s was its power against infections realized. Effective against pneumonia and other bacterias, the sulfa drugs do not actually kill the bacteria, but prevent them from multiplying.

Of the ANTIBIOTICS, penicillin is still widely used, and Penicillin G, one of the several penicillins, has the benzene ring in its molecule. Synthesis, however, has not proved practical and it is still made by growing penicillium mold. The first antibiotic to be synthesized commercially was chloromycetin (chloramphenicol), which is effective against typhoid and other intestinal infections. Salicylic acid, $HO.C_6H_4.COOH$, is the most important phenolic acid, probably more familiar as its ester methyl salicylate, better known as oil of wintergreen. The salicylic acid derivative, acetylsalicylic acid, is the correct name for aspirin.

Another important aromatic compound which has indirectly helped fight diseases in humans by killing off the disease-carrying insects is the insecticide DDT, dichlorodiphenyltrichloroethane. There are also herbicides (weedkillers) among the aromatics. They are selective, normally attacking only broad leaved plants, and work rather like plant hormones. Growth is stimulated so rapidly that the plant literally burns itself up; best known are 2.4 D (dichlorophenoxyacetic acid), and MCPA (methyl-chlorophenoxyacetic acid).

Both aniline, $C_6H_5NH_2$, and the toluidines, $CH_3.C_6H_4.NH_2$, are primary amines which are used for making dyes. They form *diazo* salts, which react with phenols and aromatic amines to give the brilliantly colored azo compounds used in around 50 per

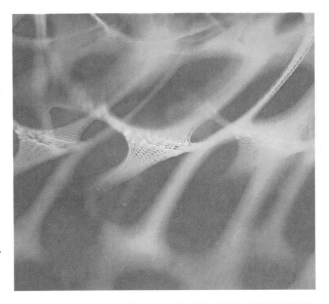

Top: As the basis of a vast range of aromatic compounds, benzene can have any or all of its hydrogen atoms replaced by other atoms or radicals to form compounds with widely differing properties. Polyester netting is a typical example.
Above: The brittle strength of porcelain (left) has little resistance to stress whereas plastic (right), such as melamine, is an extremely resilient polymer formed by the condensation of formaldehyde with melamine, and a popular domestic substitute.

cent of all nonvegetable factory dyeing processes.

These are only a few of the thousands of aromatic compounds. Daily, thousands of analytical chemists throughout the world are searching for new and useful products, sometimes based on naturally occurring, but difficult and expensive to extract, aromatic compounds like those found in textiles, structural materials and drugs.

See also: Acid; Alcohol; Amino acid; Atom and molecule; Carbon; Chemical analysis; Compound; Drug; Dyeing process; Hydrocarbon; Hydrogen; Nitrogen; Organic chemistry.

Alkali

The alkali metals are a group of ELEMENTS that are classified together in the PERIODIC TABLE, where they form group 1A. Alkaline earth metals are a similar group belonging to group 2A.

In order of increasing weight of their atoms, the alkali metals are lithium (Li), sodium (Na), potassium (K), rubidium (Rb), cesium (Cs) and francium (Fr). Sodium and potassium are the most important members of the group. All are extremely light, silver-white metals – lithium, with a density half that of water, is the lightest solid element. Cesium, the heaviest of the group, has a density of 1.87.

Alkali metals are all soft enough to be cut easily with a knife. They conduct heat and electricity well, and are easy to melt and vaporize at comparatively low temperatures, forming gases with molecules consisting of two atoms.

The metals are never found in a pure form in nature, since they are extremely reactive, and even react violently with water, forming hydroxides and releasing hydrogen. For this reason and because of their softness they are useless as structural metals, in spite of their lightness. Cesium bursts into flames even in moist air. Alkali metals therefore must be isolated from moisture, so they are stored under paraffin or in sealed evacuated containers.

Their reactivity is due to the fact that one ELECTRON of each of their atoms is unusually easy to detach, transforming the atom into an ION with a single positive charge and thus giving it a strong tendency to combine with the negative ions of other elements. Although alkali metal salts dissolve easily in water, they are extremely hard to split into the individual pure elements. Alkali metals cannot be isolated by normal ELECTROLYSIS since this involves the use of water, with which the extracted pure metal would immediately react. Instead, it is done by the electrolysis of the compound after it has been melted to make it liquid.

The tendency of the metals to give off electrons makes them useful in photoelectric cells and television camera tubes, usually in the form of a thin film deposited on glass.

Lithium, the lightest element of the group, is in some ways more like the elements of the next group in the periodic table, the alkaline earth metals. In particular, its carbonate and phosphate are only sparingly soluble in water.

Lithium carbonate is the most widely used lithium compound. It is incorporated in glass ceramics such as cooking ware and modern flat-top stoves because it imparts resistance to thermal cracking, and is used as a flux to lower operating temperatures in aluminum reduction cells.

Lithium soaps, such as lithium stearate, are used as gelling agents to solidify greases. Lithium hydride is used as a source of hydrogen, such as for meteorological balloons:

$$LiH \quad + \quad H_2O \quad \rightarrow \quad LiOH \quad + \quad H_2$$

lithium hydride   water   lithium hydroxide   hydrogen

Lithium salts are used in fireworks to give red colors. In medicine the salts have been used for the treatment of rheumatism.

Important future uses are in the manufacture of lightweight, rechargeable batteries, for example, for electric vehicles, and in the longer term lithium has a potential role in thermonuclear FUSION, a vast future energy source. The fusion system – a reaction between deuterium and tritium (heavy *isotopes* of hydrogen) – appears feasible and tritium is obtainable from lithium.

Lithium is found in naturally occurring complex silicate minerals such as spodumene, $Li_2O.Al_2O_3.4SiO_2$ – written $LiAl(SiO_3)_2$ – and in brines. Lithium is recovered from spodumene by first roasting the mineral and then bleaching it with acid. The sparingly soluble carbonate can be *pre-*

Left: Caustic potash (KOH) is recovered electrolytically from Dead Sea potassium chloride deposits at this Israeli plant.

cipitated (solidified) and dissolved in acids to form other salts. Metallic lithium is obtained by ELECTROLYSIS of the chloride, LiCl, fused with potassium chloride, KCl, to lower the melting point. The molten lithium rises to the surface and is collected under a bell to prevent it from coming into contact with the air.

Sodium is the subject of a separate article.

Potassium, K, is generally similar to sodium, although it is slightly more reactive. Like sodium, it reacts vigorously with water, releasing hydrogen, but in the case of potassium it sets the hydrogen alight and burns brilliantly.

Potassium salts are essential for the cells of all plants and animals, and plants take them from the soil. Over 90 per cent of world potash (potassium-bearing minerals) consumption is for fertilizer use. The carbonate, K_2CO_3, was first obtained by washing wood ash and evaporating the washings in pots, hence its name potash, and the dog-Latin name potassium. Potassium chloride, KCl, is used as a fertilizer, the carbonate is used in glass manufacture, and potassium hydroxide or caustic potash, KOH, is used in production of soft soap. Black gunpowder is a mixture of saltpeter, KNO_3, with charcoal and sulfur. Potassium bromide and potassium iodide are used in photography.

Rubidium was formerly recovered from processing of lithium ores but now is obtained as a by-product of cesium recovery from pollucite, a complex Cs-bearing hydrated aluminosilicate. Being heavy and easy to vaporize and ionize, rubidium and cesium would be useful for such schemes as ION propulsion in space, and magnetohydrodynamic generation of electric power.

Alkaline earth metals

In order of increasing atomic weight alkaline earth metals are beryllium (Be), magnesium (Mg), calcium (Ca), strontium (Sr), barium (Ba) and radium (Ra). Calcium and magnesium are economically the most important members in the group and the most widespread.

All the alkaline earth metals are silver-white and are good conductors of electricity and heat. They burn in air or oxygen giving a brilliant light.

The alkaline earth metals are almost as reactive as the alkali metals. The main differences are: they are harder than alkali metals; they all have a greater density than water; some of their salts, such as carbonates and sulfates, are insoluble in water (except for those of magnesium). Alkaline earth metals readily lose two electrons to become ions with two positive charges. These ions combine with negatively charged ions to form stable COMPOUNDS.

Beryllium, the lightest element in the group, is an extremely hard metal with a high strength to weight ratio. It is an excellent conductor of both

Above: When lithium is heated it gives off a bright red light, and this effect is used in the manufacture of domestic fireworks.

heat and electricity. However, it is extremely toxic and is a possible cause of cancer, as are most of its compounds. Beryllium metal is used in small quantities in the aerospace and nuclear industries. Beryllium oxide, BeO, is mainly used as a ceramic because of its low electric conductivity but high thermal conductivity.

Magnesium

Magnesium is the eighth most abundant element in the earth's crust and occurs in many rock-forming minerals and complex silicate and clay minerals. Its principal commercial sources are sea water (which contains approximately 0.2 per cent MgO), brines, magnesite, $MgCO_3$, and dolomite, $MgCO_3.CaCO_3$.

Approximately half of the magnesium metal pro-

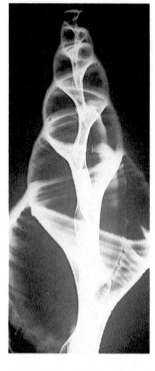

Above left: Calcium is one of the most abundant alkaline earth metals, and an essential element of many organisms. An X ray of a conch.
Above right: Evacuated vessels, incorporate getters – devices made from an alkaline earth metal (usually barium) used to remove gaseous impurities.

duced is used in aluminum alloys, which contain about 1 per cent Mg. A quarter is used in structural applications and the remainder for processes such as desulfurizing steel and cathodic protection of other metals. These processes require an active chemical reaction.

Calcium

Calcium is the fifth most abundant element in the Earth's crust and occurs widely as compounds such as calcium carbonate, phosphate, sulfate and fluoride, and in many complex silicates. Calcium is also an essential constituent of many organisms and is found in bones, teeth and shells. Calcium metal is moderately soft being harder than lead but softer than aluminum and can be cast, machined and extruded. When exposed to air it oxidizes to form a protective coating consisting of mixed oxide and nitride. It reacts with water by releasing hydrogen, but the action is comparatively slow because of the limited solubility of calcium hydroxide, better known as slaked lime.

The metal is used as a reducing agent in preparing other metals, for alloying with aluminum and magnesium, as a getter (a substance that removes gaseous impurities in high vacuum devices) and in

the separation of nitrogen from argon.

Calcium carbonate's most important and widespread forms are limestone and chalk. As a basic construction raw material it is used in large quantities to manufacture cement which is produced by roasting limestone and clay in a rotary kiln to form a *clinker* (an incombustible residue). Gypsum, $CaSO_4.2H_2O$, is added to delay the setting time of the finished cement.

Calcium carbonate is only slightly soluble in pure water but dissolves slowly in water containing carbon dioxide, derived from air, due to the formation of soluble calcium bicarbonate. In this way limestone is dissolved away. The presence of soluble calcium and magnesium bicarbonates causes temporary hardness in water, which can be reduced by the addition of slaked lime. Calcium carbonate has numerous other applications, for example, in agriculture, as a filler in paint, and in the manufacture of paper and plastics.

Calcium sulfate occurs naturally as gypsum, $CaSO_4.2H_2O$, and anhydrite, $CaSO_4$, gypsum being economically the more important. Heated gypsum loses water molecules to form gypsum plaster or plaster of Paris, $2CaSO_4.H_2O$, but rapidly rehydrates on the addition of water and reverts to gypsum. Calcium phosphate, or phosphate rock, is the only significant source of phosphorous, an important fertilizer essential for food production.

Strontium, barium and radium

Strontium is fairly rare, the main ore being celestite, $SrSO_4$. Strontium carbonate is used mainly in color TV screens to reduce X-RAY emissions and in ceramic permanent magnets for various electric applications. Strontium salts produce a characteristic brilliant crimson color and are widely used as fireworks. The radioactive isotope Sr^{-90}, a product of nuclear fission and present in nuclear fallout, is particularly dangerous as it attacks bone marrow.

Barium occurs naturally as barite, $BaSO_4$, which is soft, chemically inert and has a high specific gravity (4.48). Consequently, barite is used as a weighting agent in drilling muds to retain back pressures from oil and gas and thus prevent blowouts. Ninety per cent of world production is used for this purpose. Barite is also used as a filler in paint, rubber and plastics and in the manufacture of barium chemicals, including the carbonate, chloride, oxide, hydroxide and nitrate. The latter is used in green signal flares and tracer bullets.

Radium is extremely rare and is found closely associated with uranium ores. Its most common isotope, radium 226, has a half-life of 1620 years.

See also: Compound; Electron; Element, chemical; Ion and ionization; Periodic table; Sodium.

Alloy

The first alloy, bronze (a mixture of copper and tin) was probably discovered by accident about 3000 BC. Today, metal items are invariably made of alloys, of which there are several thousand different compositions.

An alloy is a substance composed of two or more elements of which at least one must be a metal. Such a definition is too general because no metal can be made 100 per cent pure. Therefore, the term alloy is usually reserved for those metals where other elements are intentionally incorporated.

The value of alloys over pure metals lies in the variation of blends possible and the consequent variations in strength, conductivity, temperature and corrosion resistance which can be chosen for a specific purpose. Certain pure metals may possess useful properties in their own right, but they seldom have the strength necessary for general industrial applications (for example, copper exhibits good electric conductivity but is extremely soft). Small additions of other elements can greatly improve a metal's mechanical characteristics while maintaining its other desirable properties.

Making alloys

Making alloys can be a complex process, depending on the number of different elements to be included and the precision of their required proportions. The simplest technique is to melt the elements together in the required proportions, but this is not always possible. When the melting points of the elements differ widely the element with the lower melting point evaporates extensively. Copper, for example, melts at 1983° F (1084° C). Zinc melts at 786.2° F (419° C) and begins to boil away at 1664.6° F (907° C) If, when making brass, the copper and zinc are heated together to 1983° F (1084° C), both melt but liquid zinc will already have boiled away and evapo-

Below: A ladle of molten steel is maneuvered remotely at a steelworks in Argentina. Steel, one of the most important alloys, is made from iron plus carbon and small amounts of other metals.

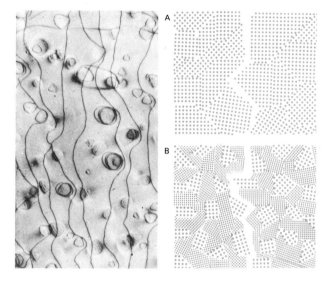

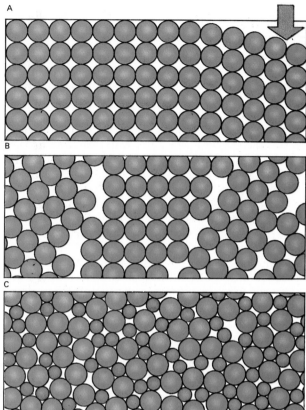

Above left: Nickel silicon alloy magnified x40,000.
Above: (A) Pure metals usually have large grains and break easily along the comparatively straight lines.
(B) An alloy with tiny grains breaks less easily.
Right: (A) A pure metal bends easily because its atoms lie in straight rows. (B) Dislocations between rows allow splits to form. (C) In a solid solution alloy, different sized atoms distort the rows and have the effect of toughening the metal.

rated in the air long before the copper attains the temperature at which it becomes molten.

To make brass, therefore, the copper is first heated until it is molten and then the solid zinc is added. The zinc dissolves quickly in the liquid copper before extensive evaporation of the molten zinc occurs.

Another technique for the blending of elements with widely differing melting points is to prepare a master alloy using part of the metal base. If, for example, an alloy is to contain 5 per cent metal A, which melts at 2000° F (1093° C), and 95 per cent metal B, which melts at 842° F (450° C), it would be difficult to melt 11 lb (5 kg) of A and then try to add 200 lb (95 kg) of solid metal B. Instead a master alloy of about 50 per cent each of A and B is made. Portions of this intermediate alloy are then melted with the remaining base.

Structure of alloys

The properties of alloys can only be explained by understanding the atomic structure of pure metals.

Although it is not obvious from their surface appearance metals are crystalline in structure, that is, their ATOMS are arranged in regular patterns, a *lattice*. This means they form a regular network at fixed points arranged in a definite geometrical pattern. Such structures are mechanically soft because their atoms are arranged as if in flat planes

or sheets which can slip over each other when an external stress is applied. If the stress is removed the planes do not slip back because pure metals have a plastic or puttylike consistency.

In reality, the ease with which atomic planes slide over each other is the direct result of the existence of defects called *dislocations* in the otherwise perfect crystal structure. The role of dislocations in the deformation of metal crystals can be best understood by looking at the problem of moving a large carpet. Simply to lift one end and pull could demand considerable effort and many hands. However, if a ruck is introduced at one end (the dislocation in this case), it can easily be pushed to the other end with the result that the carpet will have been moved by a few inches.

The presence of different types of atom in a metal crystal, whether introduced intentionally to make an alloy, or present as impurities, blocks the easy movement in dislocation and hence makes it much more difficult to deform the metal permanently. The amount and type of the added alloying metal and also the form in which it is present in the crystal structure control to a large degree the final properties of the alloy.

Alloys are prepared in their molten state, then cooled. Most metals are completely miscible – they will mix – in their molten states, and an intimate blend of such metals can be regarded as a solution of the constituent metals in each other. Metals immiscible in their molten states rarely make useful alloys, because they separate like oil and water.

The behavior of the mutual solution during solidification largely influences the properties of the resulting alloy. At one extreme, the mutual solution is undisturbed during solidification, producing what is known as a *solid solution*. Here, the alloy structure has a granular crystalline composition where each grain has the same composition as the molten mixture. Only a few pairs of metals, such as copper and nickel, can form solid solutions through the complete range of possible relative proportions.

At the other extreme, the two components can completely separate during solidification, and in this instance the resulting solid alloy will be a mixture of pure metal crystals.

More usually, there is limited solubility of each metal in the other so that the alloy consists of a mixture of two solid solutions or, as they are often called, *phases*. Take, for example, alloys of lead and tin. One phase, usually referred to as alpha, would be mainly lead with about 5 per cent tin dissolved in it, while phase beta would be mainly tin but containing 1 per cent lead. In this system the composition 62 per cent tin/38 per cent lead is significant because the alloy completely melts at a sharply defined temperature like a pure metal. If an alloy of this composition, known as the *eutectic composition*, is polished and viewed under a reflecting microscope the tin-rich beta phase appears as very finely divided particles surrounded by lead. This alloy with its sharp melting point is widely used as tinman's solder. Another alloy containing 65 per cent lead has a microstructure consisting of comparatively large grains of the lead-rich alpha phase set in more of the finely divided eutectic phase. The

melting range of this alloy extends over some 126° F (70° C) enabling it to be easily molded during solidification. For this reason it is useful in applications such as pipe joining and is commonly known as plumber's solder.

Solid solutions have two different structures, *substitutional* and *interstitial*. In substitutional solid solutions, atoms of the additive metal replace atoms in the base metal lattices usually in a random fashion. A crystal lattice built up of cubes, for example, with base metal atoms located at each corner, would have the additive metal atoms introduced haphazardly in a few of the corners. This is generally possible only where the materials have atoms of roughly the same size. But it is precisely the slight difference in atom sizes which hinders lattice movement and produces a hardening of the material, although the effect is not often very marked. Copper and nickel, for example, will produce substitutional solid solutions.

In interstitial solid solutions, atoms of the additive element are lodged within the base metal lattice rather like small balls placed inside cubes where the main metal atoms are located at each corner. Often the additive element is a nonmetal, such as carbon or nitrogen, the atoms of which are small enough to fit in the space of the lattice.

In some crystal structures the interstitial atoms form especially effective barriers to dislocations, and therefore need to be added only in small quantities. For example, interstitial dissolution of merely 0.1 per cent carbon in pure iron increases the strength of the metal more than ten-fold, thus turning the soft iron into hard steel.

There is one other type of alloy structure commonly found where two different metallic atoms form a chemical bond in some definite proportion

Left: Alloying from powders is a unique method of making some components, such as an air filter, which has a porous structure but can withstand high pressures. Because of the possibilities it offers, powder metallurgy is becoming increasingly popular for working many different types of engineering materials.

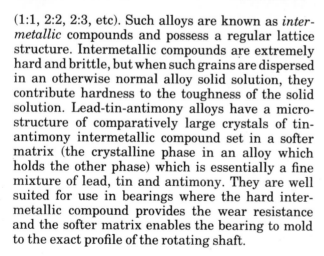

Making sand-cast alloy racing wheels. Above left: The alloy is heated to about 1330° F (720 ° C) so that it becomes molten enough to be poured.
Above right: The molten metal is poured into molds made of sand negatives sealed with wet sand and located with dowels through a funnel made of the same sand, and left to cool.
Left: The inside and the outside of the rim is machined to close tolerances, and to improve its appearance. The inside of the rim must be completely smooth to reduce the possibility of repeated punctures. After machining, the wheel undergoes crack testing: a side load of 0.5 ton – far more than the wheel will need to cope with in the normal course of riding – is placed on the hub, and the spokes are examined for any hairline cracks.

(1:1, 2:2, 2:3, etc). Such alloys are known as *intermetallic* compounds and possess a regular lattice structure. Intermetallic compounds are extremely hard and brittle, but when such grains are dispersed in an otherwise normal alloy solid solution, they contribute hardness to the toughness of the solid solution. Lead-tin-antimony alloys have a microstructure of comparatively large crystals of tin-antimony intermetallic compound set in a softer matrix (the crystalline phase in an alloy which holds the other phase) which is essentially a fine mixture of lead, tin and antimony. They are well suited for use in bearings where the hard intermetallic compound provides the wear resistance and the softer matrix enables the bearing to mold to the exact profile of the rotating shaft.

Precipitation hardening
Intermetallic compounds can also play a more subtle part in hardening alloys. One drawback of solid solution hardening is that at high temperatures the crystal lattice tends to be violently disturbed and this helps dislocations pass the barriers of alloy atoms, so that the metal becomes soft. If an alloy which under normal conditions contains a

small amount of intermetallic compound is rapidly cooled, the compound will be held in a *supersaturated solid solution*. Subsequent reheating to carefully controlled temperatures leads to the *precipitation* or depositing of the intermetallic compound in a very finely divided form throughout the solid solution. The small, hard precipitate particles are such effective barriers to dislocations that they are efficient right up to the moment when they begin to grow or redissolve.

Another very important advantage of the precipitation hardened alloys is that the supersaturated solid solution is often comparatively soft so that the alloy can easily be shaped before undergoing the final hardening treatment.

Heat treatment of steel
There is one particular type of supersaturated solid solution which plays an important part in the heat treatment of steels. When a steel is rapidly cooled from above 1500° F (800° C) by *quenching* in cold oil, a characteristic structure change, which normally occurs around 1300° F (700° C), is not given time to take place. (It involves the movement of carbon atoms through the iron to create regions of iron

carbide and therefore requires time to cool from an elevated temperature.) Under these conditions of quenching the structure change finally occurs just above room temperature in a haphazard manner, so that the carbon atoms distort the lattice to such an extent that the movement of dislocations becomes exceedingly difficult.

Steel treated in this way is known as *martensite* and is very hard indeed, but it is not particularly useful in this condition because it is also very brittle. This behavior illustrates the compromise involved in alloy design: strength can be increased by alloy additions but if it is increased beyond a certain level the metallurgist pays the price in loss of toughness. The brittleness of martensitic steel can be overcome by *tempering*, reheating to a high temperature between 1000° F (500° C) and 1300° F (700° C), followed by slow cooling. This restores toughness without too marked a loss in strength as the precipitates contribute to the hardening.

Common alloys

Bronze is the oldest alloy manufactured, and is a copper-tin blend roughly in the proportions 10-1 by weight. Another copper alloy is brass containing between 10 per cent and 45 per cent zinc by weight. *Cast iron* (pig iron) is an impure form of iron containing between 2 per cent and 4.5 per cent carbon and traces of manganese, phosphorus, silicon and sulfur. *Cast iron alloys* contain alloying elements such as nickel, chromium and molybdenum.

Steel is essentially an iron-carbon alloy containing less than 2 per cent carbon, less than 1 per cent manganese and even smaller amounts of silicon, phosphorus, sulfur and oxygen. *Alloy steels* typically contain the following elements, roughly in these proportions: chromium or nickel, 0.4 per cent or more; molybdenum, tungsten or vanadium, 0.1 per cent or more; manganese, 10 per cent or more. 18-8 *Stainless steel* contains 18 per cent chromium which forms a tough, thin, oxide film on the surface. This film protects the iron from rusting.

Nimonic alloys are based on nickel with additions of aluminum, titanium and molybdenum. They are particularly good at resisting deformation at high temperatures and find an important application in gas turbine blades. Aluminum alloys are designed for a range of specialist tasks where a strong, low-weight material is essential. Silicon, copper and magnesium are used as alloying elements, usually with small amounts of other elements such as manganese, zinc, titanium and nickel. One of the first aluminum alloys to be manufactured was Duralumin, a tough, light and strong material used in the construction of the Zeppelin airships and (in modified form) in modern aircraft. Duralumin contains about 4 per cent copper and small amounts of magnesium, manganese and silicon.

• FACT FILE •

- Shape memory alloys are special materials with a built-in "memory". Shaped components are deformed during low-temperature treatment that changes their crystal structure. When an increased temperature is applied, the alloy component regains its precise original shape.

- Continuous-wave, pulsed and Q-wave lasers can all be used to produce surface-alloy coatings. High laser power melts coatings and the main body of material so quickly that most of the work stays cool. A minimum of materials is used, and there is no weak interface between the main body and its coating.

- Amorphous alloys are noncrystalline steels made by cooling the molten metal on a spinning drum at a rate of a million degrees a second. Also known as metallic glasses, the amorphous alloys are very easily magnetized and demagnetized, making them ideal for devices such as transformers, and taperecorder heads.

Above: An automated aluminium alloy diecasting machine. Diecasting is a technique used for making large numbers of intricately shaped metal parts. The alloy is forced into the die so that it acquires the precise shape of the mold.

See also: Aluminum; Atom and molecule; Bond, chemical; Brass; Bronze; Carbon; Compound; Element, chemical; Metal; Nickel; Sheet metal; Soldering; Steel manufacture; Welding; Zinc.

Nitinol
— the thinking metal

Nitinol is one of the most extraordinary metals to be discovered this century. A simple alloy of nickel and titanium, Nitinol possesses properties that have perplexed the world of metallurgy for nearly thirty years. For Nitinol is a metal with a memory. It can be made to remember any shape into which it is fashioned, returning to it whenever it is heated.

For example, a piece of Nitinol wire bent to form a circle which is then heated and quenched will remember this shape. It may then be bent or crumpled, but on reheating, will violently untwist, reforming its original shape. This remarkable ability is called Shape Memory Effect (SME) and other alloys, such as brasses, are also known to possess it to a limited extent. No one fully understands SME, and Nitinol remains particularly perplexing, for, whenever it performs this peculiar feat, it appears to be breaking the laws of thermodynamics by springing back into shape with greater force than was used to deform it in the first place.

But not only is Nitinol capable of remembering, it also has the ability to "learn." If the heating-cooling-crumpling-reheating process is carried out sufficiently often, and the metal is always crumpled in exactly the same way, the Nitinol will not only remember its original shape, but gradually it "learns" to remember its crumpled form as well, and will begin to return to it every time it is cooled. Eventually, the metal will crumple and uncrumple, totally unaided, in response to changes in temperature and without any sign of metal fatigue.

If the force with which Nitinol changes shape could be harnessed and utilized, it could prove a valuable source of energy. Already, engineers have produced prototype heat engines that are driven by the force of Nitinol springing from one shape to another as it alternately encounters a hot and cold water supply. One of the first of these engines was produced by Ridgway Banks in 1973 and was found to be able to produce about half a watt of mechanical energy. Since then, many others have been designed with significantly higher energy outputs.

The energy from these remarkable engines is, however, not entirely free: Heat energy is required to produce the temperature differences needed to run the engine. But the optimum temperatures at which the metal reacts can be controlled by altering the proportions of nickel to titanium and some alloys will perform at room temperature. Furthermore, the necessary temperature range between the warm phase and the cold can be as little as 21° F (12° C). Thus a Nitinol engine could exploit a variety of low-grade heat sources, from geothermal springs to the coolant water used by industry.

Nitinol also holds great promise in the field of medicine. Light and resistant to corrosion, Nitinol could prove invaluable as an implant material. Its shape-changing property could aid the delicate positioning of artificial implants such as those used

Below and right: The Banks engine was one of the first devices developed to exploit the shape-memory effect of Nitinol as a source of energy. The engine is powered by Nitinol wires conditioned to straighten when heated and bend when cooled.

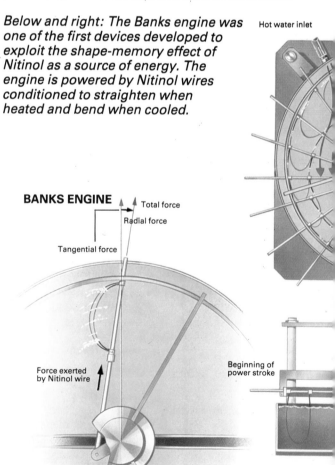

Hot water inlet

BANKS ENGINE

Total force

Radial force

Tangential force

Force exerted by Nitinol wire

Beginning of power stroke

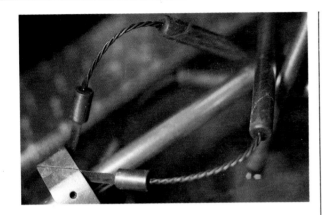

to treat spinal disorders. A slightly bent Nitinol rod could be inserted into the back close to the spine, and then, by gentle heating, it could be made to straighten with great accuracy and control, ensuring perfect alignment and support of the spine. Nitinol has also been used for artificial limb joints, bone plates and to close up bone fractures. The metal is even being considered as an engineering material for artificial hearts.

Not all of Nitinol's applications are still in the research and development stage. The aerospace industry has now been using the metal for some years as a latch and release mechanism for instrument booms on satellites. The speed and reliability of Nitinol's shape-changing response, the metal's lightness and its total resistance to metal fatigue make it an invaluable material for use in spacecraft.

This growing understanding of SME physics has led to thousands of patents being filed – for everything from super efficient heat engines to foolproof thermostats. If but a handful of these designs prove successful, Nitinol could well produce a revolution in technology as profound as the silicon chip.

Above left and right: In this elegant engine, Nitinol wires link bar weights to a spindle, and straighten when they enter hot water (left) pushing the weights outward which upsets the balance of the engine and causes the spindle to rotate.

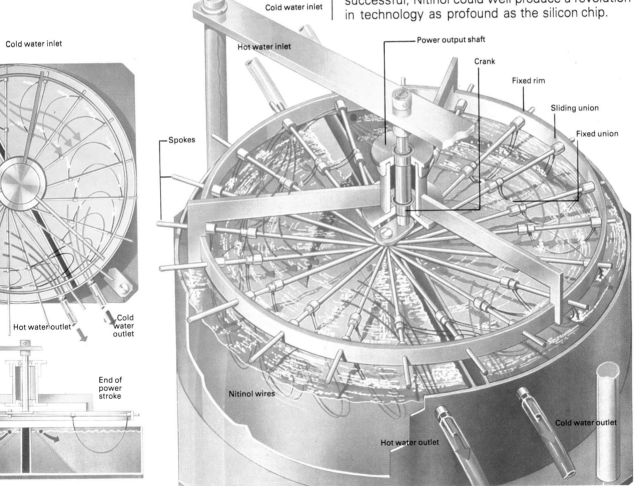

Cold water inlet

Cold water inlet

Hot water inlet

Spokes

End of power stroke

Hot water outlet

Cold water outlet

Nitinol wires

Power output shaft

Crank

Fixed rim

Sliding union

Fixed union

Cold water outlet

Hot water outlet

Alternator

Alternators are the most important of all electric machines. In all power plants – coal fired, oil fired, hydro or nuclear – it is the alternators that generate the electricity, and smaller versions are used in automobiles and on motorcycles.

An alternator is a machine for converting mechanical energy into electric power in the form of alternating current. Textbooks of physics almost invariably show a schematic diagram of an alternator as a pair of permanent magnet poles, inside which a coil of wire is rotated and the ends of the coil are shown connected to a pair of slip rings so that the current can be collected via brushes that rub on the slip rings.

The modern alternator is very different from this in construction. In the first instance permanent magnets are not used in large alternators because they give no degree of control of the magnetic field which generates the voltage. Instead the field is provided by electromagnets consisting of coils of wire fed with direct current (DC). Now the amount of power required by the field-producing magnets is of the order of, say, 20 megawatts (20 million watts). But the power generated in a large power plant alternator may be 550 megawatts. It would be highly expensive and impractical, if not impossible, to collect so much power through slip rings and brushes and accordingly alternators are built, as it were, inside-out compared with the physics text book diagram. The field magnets are rotated and the DC *excitation,* as it is called, is fed in via slip rings

and brushes, for medium-sized machines. For large machines of the 550 megawatt class, the DC is provided by a separate generator (known as an *exciter*) mounted on the same shaft, so that the magnetizing power can be fed directly to the alternator rotor along conductors, instead of having to pass through rubbing contacts.

Now the coil that receives the induced voltage due to the spinning magnets is not a simple coil on the surface of the iron yoke that surrounds the rotor, nor even a single coil sunk into a pair of slots in the iron, for to do so would be to concentrate all the heat generated by the *ohmic losses* in the coils into just two positions around the periphery, the remainder of which remains cool. The ohmic losses are the power which is dissipated because of the electric resistance of the coils. To obtain maximum output from a machine all parts of it should, in theory, heat up to the same temperature, the maximum safe temperature at which the insulating material on the coils will not break down after being in use continuously over many years.

Prime movers

Alternators tend to be of two types. The design of each type is dictated by the nature of the machine that is to drive it. These machines, generally referred to as *prime movers* tend to be either steam turbines or large water wheels driven by a natural head of water. In one notable power plant built recently in Britain, the head of water is in part

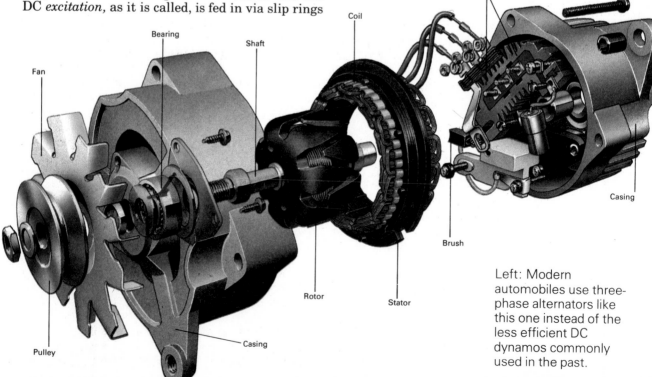

Left: Modern automobiles use three-phase alternators like this one instead of the less efficient DC dynamos commonly used in the past.

artificial. A small reservoir is emptied through a tube sunk into a mountain, with the power plant in its base. This takes place during the daytime when there is maximum demand for electricity. At night, when demand for electricity is low, the water is pumped up again to the reservoir on top of the mountain.

Water-powered alternators are slow running and therefore have many magnetic pole pairs around the rotor – as many as 50 or more. The coils on the rotos are bobbinlike and wound on iron cores that carry pole shoes on their extremities. These shoes are so shaped as to produce a sine wave of magnetic field in the gap between the stationary and the moving components.

Turbo-alternators have only two poles and because of their high speeds (up to 3600 revolutions in the U.S. and Canada, and 3000 elsewhere) the DC windings are sunk into slots in the rotor and held in by wedges. The gap between rotor and stationary outer member (or *stator*) is uniform and a sine wave of magnetic field is organized by the arrangement and connection of the DC coils on the rotor.

Distribution of stator windings

When the windings have been distributed evenly around the periphery it is no longer economical to connect the whole of one half of the machine's conductors in series, for the sine wave generated by each is slightly out of phase with that of its neighbor, and for small fractions of each cycle the induced

The turbine hall of a power plant. The turbochargers each have an output of 500 MW. In the U.S. the electric frequency is 60 Hz, so alternators run as high as 3600 rpm. Some countries have a frequency of 50 Hz, and the alternators run at 3000 rpm.

voltages in neighboring conductors will oppose each other. To minimize this loss of potential output, the windings are divided into three or more equal sections or arcs. It must be remembered, of course, that wherever such an arc terminates, an output terminal will be required and this in turn will demand a transmission line of its own, and each line will carry current of differing phase from those of other lines. The use of more than one phase is also essential to the production of good rotating fields in most large electric motors used by industry.

The windings of large alternators are cooled by a system of tubes carrying gas (often hydrogen) or water. Small alternators which are self-cooling have become popular for automobiles since electronic RECTIFIERS (which are needed for rectifying the alternator's AC output to the DC required by the electric system of the car) have become so cheap and reliable. They can be run at higher speeds than the old two-brush auto DYNAMO and thus they can give high charging currents even at engine idling speeds.

See also: Automobile; Dynamo; Electricity; Electromagnetism; Hydrogen; Magnetism; Power plant; Rectifier; Sine wave; Voltage regulator.

Altimeter

An ordinary aircraft altimeter uses a type of aneroid barometer which measures the change of air pressure at different heights. Changes in pressure due to the weather can affect its readings. But because radio waves travel at a constant speed – about 200,000 miles/second (300,000 km/s) – radar altimeters can provide an absolute measurement of an aircraft's height above ground.

By pointing a radar antenna downward, emitting a pulse of radio waves, and then seeing how long it takes for that pulse to be reflected by the Earth and return to the radar's receiving antenna on the aircraft, a measure of the distance traveled by that pulse – and hence the aircraft's height – can be calculated and displayed.

The distance the pulse has traveled can be estimated from a display on a cathode ray tube or can be measured electronically. In either case it is only really accurate at high altitudes. As the aircraft descends nearer the Earth, the time taken for the pulse to return to the aircraft becomes difficult to measure. At 1 mile (1.6 km) above the Earth, for instance, the pulse would travel the return journey in about 10 millionths of a second. A pulse would thus have to be very short in duration to differentiate between the sent and received pulses. At an altitude of 100 ft (30 m) the time between sent and received pulses would be only about 0.2 millionths of a second so pulse durations would have to be unrealistically short.

Yet it is at such heights that altitude measurement becomes critical, and so a more complicated system known as an FM CW (frequency modulated, continuous wave) radar or radio altimeter has been developed. As in the simple pulse system, signals are emitted from a radar antenna, bounced off the ground and received back at the aircraft, but here the signal is continuous, centered around some high frequency such as 4200 MHz.

This signal is arranged to increase to another frequency 200 MHz higher at a steady rate before dropping back to the original frequency.

If a pulse is sent out at the beginning of this sweep, by the time it is returned the transmitter will be emitting a high frequency. The difference depends on how long the pulse has taken to do the return journey. When these two frequencies are mixed electronically a new frequency – the difference between the two – emerges. The value of this new frequency is measured by electronic circuits. It is directly proportional to the distance traveled by the original pulse, and therefore it can be used to give a precise reading of the height.

In practice a typical FM radar today would sweep 120 times a second. Its range would be up to 10,000 ft (3000 m) over land and up to 20,000 ft (6000 m) over water, since reflections from water are clearer. Accuracy would be within 5 ft (1.5 m) for the higher ranges but would be better close to the ground – within 2 ft (0.6 m).

A major development in radar altimeters is their use on satellites to measure the surface of the Earth with unprecedented accuracy.

Below: A radar altimeter sends out a radio signal; the aircraft's height is measured by the time it takes the pulse to travel to the ground and back.

See also: Airplane; Antenna; Avionics; Barometer; Cathode ray tube; Frequency modulation; Head-up display; Inertial guidance; Radar.

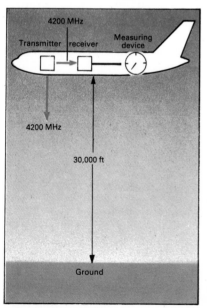

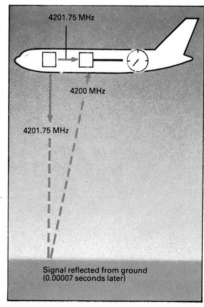

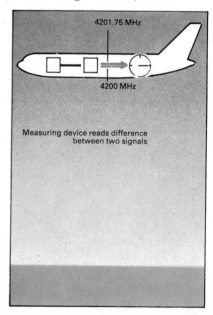

Aluminum

Aluminum, Al, is the most important element of group 3 of the PERIODIC TABLE. It is a light silver-white metal 2.7 times as heavy as water, soft but with good tensile strength, and is an excellent conductor of heat and electricity. Aluminum melts at 1220° F (660° C) and is easily cast and pressed.

Aluminum's other advantages are that it is also *ductile* – suitable for drawing into wire, and *malleable* – easy to roll into sheets and foil. An aluminum structure weighs approximately half as much as a similar steel one of comparable strength.

Apart from its strength combined with light weight, aluminum has another useful property – resistance to corrosion. This is because of a thin, hard oxide film which forms on its surface, protecting the metal from further oxidation. The oxide film can be thickened by *anodizing*, that is, OXIDATION by an ELECTROLYSIS process. The anodized film can be dyed, which is useful for architectural panels and household utensils.

Powdered aluminum is used for aluminum paint. In the powdered form it is considerably more reactive than a solid block of metal, which makes it useful as a strong reducing agent for removing oxygen in chemical processes. When a mixture of

Below: A geodesic dome structure, constructed of aluminum alloy tubing. Such buildings are both light and structurally strong.

Above: Laboratory-grown sapphire whiskers (plus aluminum oxide) are nearly perfect crystals that will withstand enormous stresses.

Above: Mining bauxite by the opencast method. Before alumina can be used in the electrolytic process it must be derived from bauxite.

aluminum powder and iron oxide is ignited, as in the Thermite Process, a large amount of heat is produced and the iron oxide is reduced to molten iron. This technique is used in welding steel and iron and in incendiary bombs.

Occurrence of aluminum

Aluminum is the third most abundant element, after oxygen and silicon in the Earth's crust, making up about 8 per cent of the total. Iron, the next most abundant element, is only 5 per cent of the total. Like so many of the metals, aluminum is not found in its pure form but associated with other elements in rocks and minerals. An aluminosilicate such as feldspar, $KAlSi_3O_8$, is the main constituent of many rocks such as granite, which is quartz and mica cemented together with feldspar. These rocks are gradually weathered and broken down by the action of carbon dioxide from the air dissolved in rainwater, resulting in the formation of kaolin, china clay, $Al_2Si_2O_5(OH)_4$. Further weathering ultimately gives bauxite, $Al_2O_3.H_2O$ or $Al_2O_3.3H_2O$, which is a hydrated form of aluminum oxide occurring widely and used for commercial aluminum extraction.

Pure aluminum oxide, also known as alumina,

Al_2O_3, is found as corundum, a crystalline, extremely hard mineral. It also occurs combined with magnetite (iron oxide), a form known as emery. Both are used as abrasives. Traces of other metal oxides present in aluminum oxide tint it to form precious stones. Chromium gives a red coloration to ruby, whereas cobalt accounts for the blue color of sapphire.

Uses of aluminum compounds

Crystalline alumina is used as an abrasive, and in powdered form for column chromatography, an analysis technique in which a liquid mixture of compounds is allowed to trickle down through a glass column packed with powdered alumina, causing the various compounds to separate at different levels. Aluminum hydroxide, $Al(OH)_3$, is used as a *mordant* in dyeing. A fabric which will not accept a dye is impregnated with the mordant. The dye reacts chemically with the mordant, forming an insoluble *lake* so dyeing the fabric. Aluminum hydroxide dissolves in acids to form salts, and in alkalis to form aluminates – few substances do both. Sodium aluminate, $NaAlO_2$, is used as a *flocculating* agent to purify water and sewage by coagulating around impurities. It is also used in paper making.

Left: Massive conductors carry the enormous current needed for the electrolysis of alumina. Nevertheless, the voltage across the cell is only about 5 volts. Because of their huge requirements, aluminum smelters are always located near cheap sources of electricity; in the past this has often been provided by hydroelectric plants, but smelters are now increasingly drawing on nuclear-generated power.

Aluminum sulfate, $Al_2(SO_4)_3.18H_2O$, is widely used as a source of aluminum hydroxide. It is also used together with sodium carbonate in foam-type fire extinguishers. It forms double sulfates with other metals. They are known as ALUMS, such as potassium alum, $K_2SO_4.Al_2(SO_4)_3.24H_2O$. Alums are used in manufacturing processes such as dyeing and in paper making.

When chlorine gas is passed over aluminum foil a white solid, aluminum chloride, Al_2Cl_6, is formed. This is an important CATALYST in the synthesis of aromatic compounds.

Uses of aluminum

Aluminum is now the second most widely used metal, coming after iron. Aluminum and its ALLOYS, such as duralumin, are used as structural metals for a wide variety of products from aircraft to cooking utensils. Aluminum foil is made by hot rolling followed by cold rolling, and is used in food packaging. Foil is also being used to replace copper wire in electric windings. Other electric applications for aluminum foil include being used in CAPACITORS. Cross-country electric cables consist of a steel core surrounded by pure aluminum. Pure polished aluminum is an excellent reflector, and does not tarnish. Aluminum mirror reflectors are used on large astronomical telescopes.

Aluminum alloys have been used in buildings for cladding panels, door and window frames, roofs, and Venetian blinds. Diecast aluminum cylinder blocks are used in a number of cars. Other forms of transportation where these alloys have been successfully incorporated are the superstructure of large ships such as the QE2, and on a much smaller scale, but where weight saving is equally important, in air cushion vehicles.

Aluminum extraction

Pure metallic aluminum does not occur naturally. Being a highly reactive element, it is always found tightly combined with other elements, and it must be separated from them chemically during the process of extraction.

Large-scale aluminum production depends on the reduction of aluminum oxide, alumina, to aluminum metal by the process of ELECTROLYSIS. Alumina can be easily obtained from bauxite, the main ore of aluminum. Bauxite is a claylike, amorphous material formed by the weathering of silicate rocks, and often contains other metallic oxides, mostly of iron. Although bauxite is the only practical source of aluminum, the element is also found in small quantities in other substances as diverse as pottery, clay and emeralds. The alumina content of bauxite varies widely and only high grade ores with more than 45 per cent alumina are worth mining.

Before alumina can be used in the electrolytic process it has to be separated from the other oxides

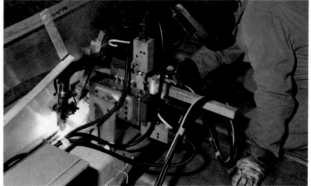

Left: Paper coated with aluminum oxide is a powerful industrial abrasive used in many industries. Such high-speed belts are used for shaping and finishing.
Above: Arc welding is the commonest method used to hold aluminum structures together. An AC power supply strikes an arc between the welding electrode and the workpiece, the high temperature generated by the arc melting the surfaces to be joined. High currents are necessary for arc welding of aluminum.

that make up bauxite. Crushed bauxite is digested in a strong caustic soda solution at high temperature. The alumina reacts with the hot hydroxide solution and forms soluble sodium aluminate in the caustic soda. All the impurities remain undissolved and can be filtered off. The aluminum is recovered from the solution as an oxide strongly combined with three molecules of water. So strong is the bond between the aluminum oxide and the water molecules that it must be heated to 2372° F (1300° C) to drive off the combined water, finally giving anhydrous alumina, Al_2O_3.

Aluminum from alumina

To break the strong bond between the oxygen and the aluminum molecule requires a large input of energy and this is provided by a low voltage, high amperage current of electricity passed through a bath containing molten alumina.

Pure alumina melts at 3632° F (2000° C), a very high and impractical temperature to maintain in an industrial plant. However, by dissolving the alumina in *cryolite* (Na_3AlF_6), a double salt of sodium and aluminum, the working temperature of the process can be brought down to a far more manageable 1830° F. Even so, about two-thirds of the electricity used goes to keep the solution molten.

The alumina-cryolite solution is contained in a heavy metal *cell* or pot with massive carbon CATHODES in the base connected to the negative side of the direct current power supply. Carbon ANODES, connected to the positive side of the supply and normally made in blocks about 2 ft (0.6 m) square by about 4 ft (1.2 m) long, are suspended above the

pot and lowered into the electrolyte during extraction. The voltage across the solution is only about five volts but, since its resistance is low, the current is very high. Heavy conducting leads provide the power to each pot and supply the rows in which scores of pots are arranged. A typical modern aluminum smelter will have several hundred pots in total, each one holding perhaps 20 tons.

When the current is turned on, the carbon in the electrodes reacts with the alumina to produce free aluminum and carbon dioxide:

$$2Al_2O_3 + 3C \rightarrow 4Al + 3CO_2$$
alumina   carbon   aluminum   carbon dioxide

Molten aluminum sinks to the bottom of the pot and collects over the cathode. It is periodically siphoned off into insulated containers and taken to holding furnaces, where it may be alloyed to give it special properties. From there, it is normally cast into billets, slabs or ingots for further processing.

The carbon comes from the anode, which is consumed by the process. As it turns into carbon dioxide, the anode is slowly lowered into the cryolite solution until it is exhausted. Large amounts of electricity are used by this process; the power used by a typical family household in a year would not supply much more than a quarter of a ton of the metal. Because of this, aluminum smelters are always near cheap sources of power. In the past, this has frequently been hydroelectric power but some smelters now draw heavily on nuclear as well as coal or oil generated electricity. With the cost of power increasing, there has been recent interest in

Left: Electron beam welding. Although the hard diode film present on the surface of aluminum offers excellent protection against corrosion and other damage, it also prevents proper welding if it is not removed. Once this has been done, welding can be carried out; the main methods are arc and resistance welding. The electron beam method, in which the weld must be formed in a complete vacuum, is used for tiny regulated circuits and thick material.

developing other methods of extraction which are viable on a commercial scale. A chloride method has been tried in the U.S., and a process using lime is also being developed. But these and other new methods have not been as successful as hoped and they only account for a minute fraction of total production.

The aluminum from the electrolytic process is 99.0 per cent to 99.8 per cent pure, the main impurities being traces of iron and silicon. Even purer aluminum, of 99.99 per cent purity, can be obtained for special purposes by further refining.

Aluminum welding

The hard, persistent oxide film always present on the surface of aluminum offers excellent protection against corrosion and other damage. The film, however, prevents proper welding of aluminum if it is not first removed or broken up.

In general, the techniques employed in welding aluminum and its alloys are similar to those used for welding steel, but with modifications to overcome the difficulties caused by the oxide film.

These difficulties occur because of the properties of the film. It has a melting point above 3600° F (2000° C); it is insoluble in solid or in molten aluminum; it resists ordinary welding fluxes; and it reforms as soon as it is removed. Less important difficulties arise because aluminum conducts heat about five times better than steel does. More heat is conducted away, so more heat must be applied. In addition, aluminum has a higher electric conductivity than steel and so arc welding demands higher currents.

The basic methods of welding aluminum are *gas, arc, resistance* and, to a limited extent, *electron beam* welding. Arc and resistance welding account for about 90 per cent of all aluminum welds.

Electron beam welding

Electron beam welding of aluminum is practical for both tiny integrated circuits and quite thick material, and has been widely used in the aerospace industry. Another technique, ultrasonic welding, is limited to very thin materials, and is used principally for joining aluminum foil. Arc welding, the most widely used technique, depends on striking an electric arc between an electrode and the workpiece, using the workpiece as part of the electric circuit.

See also: Alloy; Bond, chemical; Conduction; Electrolysis; Element, chemical; Metal; Oxidation and reduction; Rolling, metal; Welding.

Ambulance

With the recent discovery that up to 25 per cent of all emergency fatalities die while on their way to the hospital in the ambulance, it was realized that the standard of care, and consequently the design of the ambulances, would have to be improved.

Ambulances are rarely custom-built, but are converted from a standard design of truck or car. For example, in the U.S. the Cadillac hearse chassis provides great passenger comfort though little space for equipment.

It is vital to have space and equipment in the ambulance to provide emergency first care for patients, but it has been found in practice that emergency mobile operating rooms are inefficient. Performing a delicate operation at the scene of a road accident, with nearby heavy traffic and the lack of full hospital facilities, is too hazardous to be worthwhile. Consequently, ambulances are designed simply to transport their patients rapidly in the greatest possible comfort, while carrying enough equipment to deal with the most common causes of ambulance fatalities. With the advent of new computerized diagnostic machines, however, it may be possible to provide doctors at the hospital with a complete patient profile on arrival at an emergency room, saving much valuable time – and, in some cases, lives – in the operating room.

Ambulance layout

Any ambulance needs plenty of interior space. It must carry bulky gear such as suction apparatus to clear blocked airways and oxygen equipment to aid respiration, and still have enough space to enable full first aid procedures to be carried out. For these reasons, large custom-designed vehicles are of more use than converted automobiles, though the latter may well give greater comfort.

Using a commercial vehicle as a basis usually results in a harsh ride. To improve this, a well-designed ambulance needs a long wheelbase, so that the patient does not have to lie over the rear axle; a low CENTER OF GRAVITY, to prevent the body of the vehicle from rolling when cornering at speed, and a low floor, to make loading of stretchers easier. These considerations mean that front wheel drive is necessary, since this does not require a bulky transmission shaft leading to the rear wheels. By using automatic transmission, jerky and awkward gear

Below: Ambulances attend an automobile accident. Although long wheelbase car chassis types, like the Cadillac hearse body, provide a smoother ride, truck designs have more space for vital equipment.

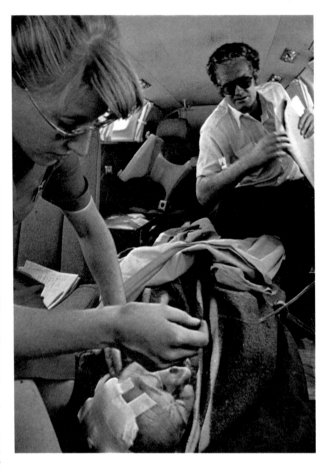

Above: Many people in remote, sparsely populated or inaccessible areas rely on light aircraft flying ambulances as their only efficient means of transport, particularly in emergency situations.

shifts are avoided, making things easier for both patient and driver.

When adapting a chassis to an ambulance, an entire body is often fabricated from glass reinforced plastics or glass fiber, which is light, nonrusting and can be molded to any desired shape. Storage cupboards and the bottle holders for saline or blood drips can also be made from this material.

Despite being adapted from commercial vehicles, ambulances are required to exhibit high performance and reliability. The wheels in particular take a great strain, and have to be inspected regularly for signs of cracking.

Electric equipment

Ambulances must have a comprehensive system for warning of their approach. A London ambulance, for example, has 13 lights to the front, 11 to the rear, and a two-tone siren. To run these, and to provide power for the suction unit, premature baby unit and bright internal lighting, a heavy-duty alternator is needed.

One point which was overlooked in the past is that flashing lights are needed at the level of car rear windows, so that automobile drivers realize what sort of vehicle has suddenly appeared in their rear-view mirror.

In addition to the standard first care equipment, ambulances may be provided with electronic monitoring recorders so that on arrival at the hospital the doctors can discover quickly what treatment the patient will need. Most vehicles are also equipped with two-way radios to enable them to be deployed more efficiently.

The last word

Probably the world's most sophisticated ambulance is run by the International Grand Prix Medical Service, which attends motor races all over Europe. At these, hospital facilities may not be immediately available. Fifty feet (15 m) in length, the ambulance is virtually a miniature dust-free, air conditioned hospital. It has a battery powered X-ray machine, a hydraulic lift to bring stretcher patients into the unit without tilting them, a refrigerated blood bank and an operating room.

This massive device can be driven at up to 70 mph (113 km/h) although it weighs 24 tons. It has its own electric generators and a self-contained hot and cold water supply.

See also: Battery; Electronics in medicine; Glass fiber; Heart-lung machine; Operating room; Radio; Siren; Surgery; Suspension; X ray.

Amino acid

Amino acids are the building blocks of which protein MOLECULES are made, and so are the basic structural material of all living matter.

Although there are many millions of different kinds of proteins, there are only 21 amino acids, the molecules of which are linked together in a large number of different ways, and often in huge numbers, to form each protein molecule. For example, hemoglobin consists of the protein *globin*, which is formed of 574 amino acid molecules, and a complex organic compound, *hem,* which gives blood its characteristic red color.

Animals are constantly using up protein through processes such as excretion and the growth of hair and nails. As a result, they need a constant supply of amino acids which can be used where required for energy, and for building into protein. They do this by taking in protein, hydrolyzing it (breaking it down) into separate amino acids through the action of ENZYMES in the digestive tract, and rebuilding them into the proteins that are needed. Enzymes are themselves proteins, and function like CATALYSTS in the body, speeding up the various biochemical reactions.

The 21 amino acids are valine, leucine, isoleucine, threonine, methionine, phenylalanine, tryptophan, lysine, glycine, alanine, serine, cysteine, tyrosine, aspartic acid, asparagine, glutamic acid, glutamine, arginine, histidine, cistine and proline. The first eight are essential to human beings, because the body cannot synthesize them from other substances. A lack of any of them in the diet causes malnutrition. Vegetarian diets, unless carefully planned, tend to lack some of the essential substances. The list of essentials varies slightly for different animals.

The general amino acid formula is $R.CH.NH_2COOH$, with R standing for either a hydrogen atom (in the case of the simplest amino acid, glycine) or a more complex organic radical or group of atoms. This formula gives the amino acid an unusual property which makes it valuable in a living cell.

The formula contains both the acidic or carboxyl group, $-COOH$, and the alkaline or amino group, $-NH_2$. When an amino acid molecule dissolves in water it ionizes (becomes an ION) but because the carboxyl group has a negative charge and the amino group a positive charge, the resulting ion is electrically neutral. This is called a *zwitterion.*

If a positively charged ion, such as a hydrogen ion (H^+) from an acid, is introduced into an amino acid solution, it is attracted to the negatively charged portion of the amino acid zwitterion, neutralizing it and leaving it with only its positive charge. Similarly, a negative ion such as a hydroxyl ion (OH^-) from an alkali is attracted to the positively charged portion of the amino acid molecule.

This ability of amino acids to collect any stray positive and negative (and therefore acidic or alkaline) ions allows them to act as buffers in living cells, maintaining the delicately balanced pH (a measure of acidity or alkalinity) which the cells must have in order to function.

See also: Atom and molecule; Cell; Protein.

Below: Magnified crystals of asparagine, an alkaloid found in asparagus, beets and other vegetables.

Ammeter

An ammeter measures electric current, the unit of which is the ampere (A). For small currents, such as in most electronic circuits, the milliampere (mA) and microampere (μA) are used.

The principle on which ammeters work is that current passing along a wire creates a magnetic field around it, the strength of which is proportional to the current. The force of the field around the wire moves a pointer over a scale by an amount depending on the size of the current.

There are three basic types of ammeter: *moving coil, moving iron (or moving magnet)* and *digital*. The moving coil type has a linear scale – its divisions are equally spaced – whereas the moving magnet type has a nonlinear scale. The moving coil ammeter has three basic components: a permanent magnet, an electromagnet and pointer assembly and a helical spring. The electromagnet comprises a flat, rectangular coil formed on a cylindrical soft iron core, on which the pointer is secured. This assembly constitutes the moving coil of the instrument, and it is pivoted, usually on jeweled bearings, so that the coil lies at right angles to the permanent magnet's field.

The current to be measured is passed through the coil, producing a magnetic field in opposition to that of the permanent magnet. The reaction between the two fields causes the coil and pointer to rotate over the scale. The rotation assembly is held in check by the spring. Without the spring, the assembly would rotate until the two magnets no longer opposed each other. It resists the rotation and restores the pointer to the zero current position when the current is switched off. Every position on the ammeter's scale corresponds to a particular force and hence to a particular current.

In this form, the ammeter measures direct current (DC) up to a fixed maximum known as *full scale deflection* (fsd), which can be as low as 25 μA in sensitive instruments. The range can be extended by the addition of *shunt resistors*, which are connected across the coil. The shunt carries most of the current, so only a small proportion flows through the coil. The accuracy of such instruments is frequently within one or two per cent of fsd, but much higher accuracies are achieved in laboratory instruments. To measure alternating current (AC), RECTIFIERS are connected in the circuit to convert AC into DC, which is then passed to the coil.

A simpler and cheaper, though less sensitive and less accurate, method of measuring AC is to use a moving-iron ammeter. In this instrument, the pointer is attached to a spring or counterbalance weight and to a piece of soft iron. Another piece of iron is fixed near the first. When the current to be

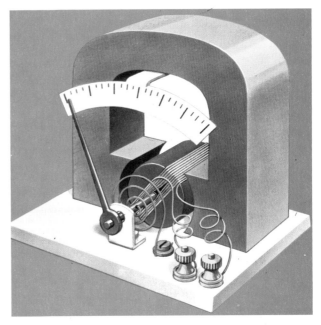

Top: Moving-coil ammeter. The current to be measured goes through the coil via terminals, establishing a magnetic field which opposes the field of the permanent magnet. The coil rotates against the force of the spring, moving the pointer over the scale.
Above: Modern digital multimeters. which measure resistance as well as current, are more reliable.

measured passes through a coil surrounding the whole meter movement, magnetic fields are formed around the two pieces of iron, causing them to repel each other. The pointer moves against the retaining spring, but its movement is nonlinear because the repulsive force falls off as the distance between the two pieces of iron increases.

See also: Conduction; Electricity; Electromagnetism; Rectifier; Resistor; Watt meter.

Ammonia

One of the most important industrial processes is the manufacture of ammonia, which is needed for fertilizers, the manufacture of nitric acid, for use as a refrigerant, and as a cleaning agent.

Ammonia is manufactured from the gases nitrogen and hydrogen by the Haber-Bosch process. In most modern plants the nitrogen is obtained from the air, of which it makes up 78 per cent by volume, and the hydrogen from natural gas.

Below: Ammonia produced by passing heated hydrogen and nitrogen through iron oxide.

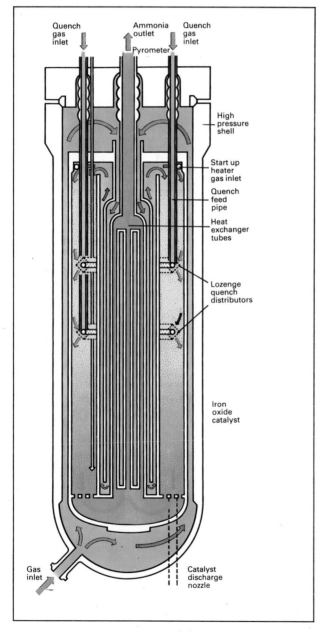

$$N_2 + 3H_2 \rightarrow 2NH_3$$
nitrogen   hydrogen   ammonia

The impetus to make ammonia came after Crookes' prediction in 1898 that the world's supplies of nitrogen compounds, which were in the form of Chile saltpeter, were being used up and unless an alternative source was found the world would starve for lack of fertilizer. A German chemist, Fritz Haber, managed successfully to synthesize ammonia under high pressure using a catalyst. A chemical engineer, Karl Bosch, later developed the laboratory technique into a full-scale commercial process.

Theoretically, low temperature combined with high pressure are required to produce ammonia, but in practice temperatures of about 900° F (500° C) and pressures from 150 to 1000 times atmospheric pressure are used. This is because below 900° F (500° C) the rate at which equilibrium is reached is too slow. Unfortunately, at a higher temperature the amount of ammonia produced is low, around 20 per cent at 250 atmospheres and around 50 per cent at 800 atmospheres. By using a CATALYST the rate of reaction can be speeded up.

The catalyst is usually iron oxide which is often mixed with a small quantity of a promoter such as aluminum sesquioxide to increase its effectiveness. The iron oxide is reduced by the hydrogen to spongy pure iron when the process is started up. Over a period the catalyst gradually loses its effectiveness as it becomes poisoned by traces of carbon dioxide, carbon monoxide and sulfur compounds.

In the process itself the catalyst is packed into catalyst beds inside the steel reaction vessel which is designed to withstand very high pressure. The steel must also be resistant to attack from hydrogen especially under the high temperature and pressure conditions. The nitrogen and hydrogen gases are purified, compressed, and passed through a warm-up heater before entering the converter.

The ammonia gas formed is liquefied by passing it through pipes cooled by cold water. Unconverted nitrogen and hydrogen present are not liquified and are recycled.

Other methods of preparing ammonia commercially are from coal gas, and the cyanamide process where calcium cyanamide is sprayed with water to remove traces of calcium carbide, and is then treated with superheated steam which causes it to decompose into ammonia and calcium carbonate.

$$CaCN_2 + 3H_2O \rightarrow 2NH_3 + CaCO_3$$
calcium   water   ammonia   calcium
cyanamide   carbonate

See also: Acid; Catalyst; Compound; Fertilizer; Hydrogen; Liquefaction; Nitrogen; Refrigeration.

Ammunition

Ammunition is basically any explosive device, from the tiny cartridge in a starting pistol to a massive ten-ton bomb.

The word ammunition is derived from the Latin *munire,* meaning to fortify, and originally meant fortifications and the tools of war. From this stems a modern definition that ammunition is any military device which includes components filled with EXPLO-SIVE, smoke-producing, incendiary (fire producing) or pyrotechnic (illuminating) compositions. However, this definition would exclude many other items, for example, shotgun cartridges, distress and signaling rockets, engineering explosives, chemicals such as tear gas, aircraft ejection seat cartridges, and even fireworks, all of which can be considered as types of ammunition.

Explosives
All ammunition contains explosive material in one form or another, and the way they function and release their energy can be precisely controlled.

Explosives are substances that can be converted into hot gases or volatile products, and in the process exert a sudden pressure on the surroundings. The speed with which this happens determines the precise application of the explosive substance. High explosives react fast, usually within a few millionths of a second, and produce a sudden and disruptive increase in pressure which causes a severe shock wave. The tremendous power released by this detonation can be used to burst a shell into small, lethal fragments. Low explosives are slower, taking a few thousandths of a second to react. The pressure produced can be used in a gun, for example, to propel a shell.

Typical high explosives as used in shells, bombs, land and sea mines, grenades and demolition work are TNT, gelignite, hexogen, tetryl and PETN. Nitrocellulose is a typical low explosive used in most modern guns as a propellant.

Gun ammunition
Ammunition for guns, whatever the size, comprises

Below: An SS2 antitank missile is fired from a Westland Scout helicopter. In normal combat situations, these weapons are fired from the air.

AMMUNITION

Fuze

High explosive filling

Steel shell

Driving band

Fixed round with explosive shell

Propellant

Cartridge case

Primer

Gliding metal jacket

Lead antimony core

Small arms round with bullet

Propellant

Cartridge case

PRIMER DETAIL

Flash holes

Gunpowder

Metal ball

Sensitive explosive

Cup

PRIMER DETAIL

Anvil

Cup

Cap composition

Lead alloy core

TRACER BULLET

Tracer compositions

Hole

Cardboard disc

Shot

Rolled paper tube

SHOTGUN CARTRIDGE

Wad

Propellant

Brass end

Cap

Top: A comparison of artillery and rifle ammunition, with details of the detonators, and (above) a tracer bullet and a shotgun cartridge.

a propellant charge and a projectile. The two items may be secured permanently together (fixed), supplied as individual items and put together before loading (semifixed), or kept and loaded separately (separate loading). The deciding factors are, first, the method of gas sealing or *obturation* adopted and, second, the gun's barrel size or *caliber*. The charge is sealed off in the gun's chamber either by means of a pad fitted to the breach, or by enclosing the propellant in a cartridge case. Gas pressure from the burning propellant expands the pad or the case to seal off the rear of the charge completely. The projectile fits snugly in the barrel, preventing a forward leak of gas. As the *bore* (internal diameter) of the gun increases, the charge and projectile become heavier and more cumbersome to handle, and it is necessary to load them separately.

Components

A round of ammunition comprises the propellant or charge and the projectile or shell. For a typical fixed round, the cartridge case is usually made of brass, 70 parts copper to 30 of zinc. The brass is pressed into shape in a series of stages, which harden and strengthen the metal. By alternately working and annealing, at about 1112° F (600° C), the case can be made thick and hard at the base, to take the initiating cap and primer and to withstand the forces of loading and extraction. The center section is made softer, so it can expand and seal against the chamber wall, and the nose is harder so it can be crimped firmly to the shell. Other materials, such as steel, aluminum and plastics, and cheaper methods of construction, are in use today, but they have only limited application. However, progress is being made toward developing a small arms round with such durable propellant explosive that no cartridge case is necessary and the entire charge section is consumed when the round is fired.

The propellant may be in the form of small grains, short or long cords, or a solid block perforated by slots of holes to control the speed of burning. It is ignited by the primer. This comprises a small quantity of a very sensitive explosive which is initiated, or detonated, either when the striker pinches it between the cup and anvil, or by an electric impulse. The flash is passed to a few grains of gunpowder, which ignites to set off the propellant – the main charge.

The shell or projectile has three main components: the high-explosive filling, the driving band and the fuze. Shells are normally forged from a good quality steel, the final shape being the result of three or more operations and some machining to achieve the required tolerances. The projectile's shape is determined by a number of factors. For a stable flight, it should be no longer than five times the caliber. For low skin friction, it should be

Above: Machine gun tracer and mortar fire at night. The bright paths of the ammunition trajectories can be used to sight in on an enemy position.
Left: British artillerymen load a 105 mm light gun. Note the high angle of elevation, for a short range target.

smooth and the base should be streamlined to reduce aerodynamic drag. The driving band is a copper ring forced into a groove cut around the lower section of the body. Its tasks are to provide a good gas seal in front of the charge, to seat the projectile in the bore, and to engage the spiral rifling of the gun barrel to make the shell spin. The shell body is filled with high explosive, for example, TNT. This is done by pouring molten explosive into the cavity, taking care to ensure no empty spaces are formed on cooling. A ratio of 15 per cent explosive to the total shell weight is normal.

The explosive in the projectile is itself the propellant of the warhead. At the simplest level it splinters its casing into lethal fragments of shrapnel but, even then, the case may be notched in sections to create a specific shape of shrapnel. When a shell is used against armored fighting vehicles the explosive may be distributed through the warhead in a certain way which is designed to direct all its force into a narrow channel capable of piercing armor plate. There are also cluster munitions which carry a mass of submunitions to be released over the target. The U.S. M483 bomblet round carries a cluster of 88 bomblets which are independent warheads capable of piercing armor and producing antipersonnel fragments.

To achieve greater range, modern artillery shells may be rocket assisted. This involves using part of the shell body to incorporate a rocket motor, which is ignited at the highest point of the trajectory by a time delay mechanism. This additional impulse can increase the maximum range by about 30 per cent, though the accuracy may be reduced. An alternative system is the base bleed method, in which the hollow base of the shell contains a burning composition. The gases of combustion are leaked out to fill the low pressure area behind the shell and so reduce aerodynamic drag. Base bleed techniques can improve maximum range by up to 25 per cent, without impairing accuracy. Another method of improving a projectile's range is to improve its aerodynamic profile by streamlining it and arranging for it to discard the driving band or an outer casing when it leaves the gun barrel. All improvements designed to increase a projectile's range carry the penalty of lessening its payload.

The accuracy of certain munition types has been vastly improved by building guidance mechanisms into the projectile. Laser guided bombs or shells rely upon a designator to illuminate the target with a laser beam. A sensor built into the head assembly picks up reflections from the target and homes in on it by passing messages through an electronic assembly that twists the wings and fins of the projectile to cause it to turn onto the required path. Infrared or magnetic homing systems are as practicable as laser illumination but all are expensive

and reduce the payload by taking up space in the projectile body.

Fuzes

The fuze is the last component to be fitted to the shell. It can be the most dangerous component in the round, and is designed not to explode during firing, when it is typically subjected to gas pressures of 20 tons per square inch and accelerations of 20,000 g. Yet it must function reliably when the shell strikes the target. Like the cartridge the fuze contains an explosive train: a striker sets off a detonator, the impulse is passed to a less sensitive but more forceful explosive contained in a pellet, and the detonation wave from this pellet sets off the main filling. Fuzes are extremely intricate and are designed to respond to the forces of firing and flight. The mechanism can be likened to that of a combination lock: it is unlocked by the special signatures of the forces imposed by the gun and no other stimulation is normally required.

Fuzes may act either on impact or after a short delay, allowing time for the shell to penetrate the target. When attacking targets in the open, it may be advantageous to burst the shell above, so as to deliver fragments and blast downward. This requires a time fuze, which bursts the shell at a specified time after firing. Timing may be mechanical, electronic or by the burning of a pyrotechnic train. Alternatively, proximity fuzes may be used. These employ RADAR techniques to detect the target and burst the shell at the height for best effect.

For separate loading ammunition, where the gun's breech mechanism provides the rear seal, the charge is composed of sticks of propellant bound together inside a cloth bag. Sewn to one end is an igniter pad holding a small quantity of gunpowder. This is ignited by the flash from a small brass cased cartridge fitted into a vent in the breech block.

Semifixed and separate rounds are necessary on guns from which various shell velocities are required, for example, to produce a specific trajectory to cross an obstacle (such as a hill or forest) behind which the target is hidden. For rounds of this kind, the charge is subdivided into small bags, which may be fired in various combinations in order to achieve the desired trajectory of the projectile.

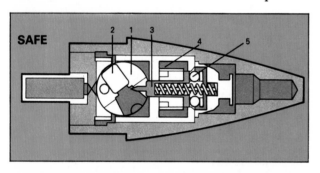

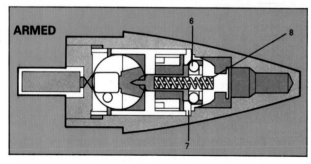

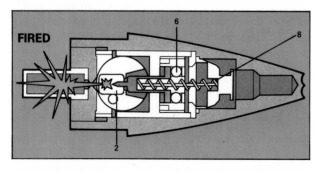

Left: The parts of a fuze: (1) Shutter. (2) Detonator. (3) Firing pin. (4) Flat spiral spring. (5) Split collet. (6) Balls. (7) Support collar. (8) Firing pin spring.
The shell is safe (top) when the shutter is locked. It becomes armed (center) when the spinning of the shell forces the balls up the support collar, pulling the firing pin forward and compressing the spring. It fires (bottom) when impact drives the balls back, freeing the firing pin to strike the detonator which sets off the filling.

Other types of ammunition

This basic design is modified to produce a wide range of ammunition rounds. Small arms rounds do not need gunpowder in the primer, because the small amount of cap composition is sufficient to ignite the propellant. The bullet is made of a lead–antimony alloy core coated with a gilding metal jacket. On firing, the jacket, which is slightly over caliber in size, performs the function of a driving band. Armor-piercing shells have a core of steel or tungsten carbide instead of lead alloy. Tracer bullets contain compositions that burn in flight, making it possible to see the bullet's trajectory. This allows the aim to be improved.

For shotgun cartridges, the single projectile is replaced by a quantity of small lead balls (shot), their size and number depending on the range and spread required. The gun works at low pressures, so the case need not be made entirely of brass. Only the rear portion holding the cap, which is bonded to a rolled paper or plastic tube containing the propellant and shot, is made of brass. The front end is closed by a cardboard disc, and the whole is lacquered to prevent moisture entering the charge.

The design of ammunition for guns is complicated by the large number of components and the violent conditions of firing.

See also: **Antiaircraft gun; Armor-piercing shell; Automatic weapon; Ballistics; Bomb; Bullet; Gun; Machine gun; Missile; Rifle.**

Above: An array of the weaponry available to the European Panavia Tornado all-purpose warplane on its diverse range of missions.

• FACT FILE •

- In 1834 in an exhaustive test to weigh the efficiency of percussion caps against that of flintlock flash-pans, 6000 rounds were fired from flintlock muskets, and 6000 rounds from percussion guns. The flintlocks misfired on average once in every six shots, while the percussion guns only misfired once in every 166 shots.

- The U.S. Army's 152 mm gun fires exploding canisters, each of which contains 10,000 steel darts called flechettes. On detonation, the flechettes have an effective range of 1300 ft (400 m). Untraceable by X ray, plastic flechettes have also been used to optimise wound damage.

- In World War II the Germans developed rocket-assisted shells called R-Granats, which were used in a railway-mounted artillery piece. Their maximum range was 53 miles (80 km).

Chemical ammunition

Now in preparation for future campaigns of warfare are chemicals so deadly that they could kill if a drop the size of a pin head settled on your skin. These so-called nerve gases have been in existence since before World War II, but they have been given a new potency by the introduction of devices known as binary weapons.

Binary weapons consist of two containers in which are two separate chemicals. Isolated from one another, they are as harmless in some cases as common salt. Mixed, they become nerve gas, blood agents or vesicants. All can kill or disable within a few seconds.

Predelivery, binary agents are safer than the gas shells, chemical bombs or rockets that they are replacing. In such projectiles the agent is stored in a container and spread by an explosive charge either as it approaches the target or when the shell hits the ground. In all of these systems there is the slight danger of an accident before the weapon is fired — while it is in transit or storage. There is also occasionally the danger of seepage through the walls of the projectile. In a binary weapon the agents are mixed only when the shell is in flight — this can be actuated by a time delay, by a radar signal which fires an explosive charge within the body of the shell or by air pressure.

Binary systems can also be fitted to aircraft to be sprayed as an aerosol. The two chemicals are housed in separate tanks and the aircraft makes a fast, low pass over a target area. The major advantage of this system is that it puts a greater concentration of the agent into the target area in a

Above: U.S. M256 detector kit which can detect and indentify chemical agents in time for effective countermeasures to be taken.
Right: Troops training to get accustomed to wearing NBC (Nuclear, Biological, Chemical) protection clothing, now a priority in most NATO and Warsaw Pact forces.

shorter time than explosive shells or rockets.

The binary system has an added advantage when the chemicals become due for disposal. Instead of having to dispose of a single highly toxic poison, the two separate sections of a binary system can be buried or dumped at sea with less risk of pollution.

Binary weapons are also easier to protect in peace time. To exploit their lethality, a terrorist group would not only have to secure both components, but they would also need to know how to mix them without poisoning themselves.

Though binary weapons are safer, there is a

sinister suggestion that they could be used to deliver more lethal agents than have previously been considered safe for operational use. If the agent only becomes effective in flight, chemicals too deadly for normal systems could be used because they would become dangerous only in the planned target area.

Even now the existing agents are dangerous enough. The nerve gases attack a chemical in the body called cholinesterase. This enzyme controls the muscles by breaking down acetylcholine, the chemical which causes muscular contraction. In the absence of acetylcholine the body goes into spasms and the victim dies from asphyxiation. To add to their effect, nerve gases are colorless and odorless and so undetectable.

The nerve agent that has been used by the West since the Allies discovered and took over German stocks in 1945 is GB (Sarin). The U.S.S.R. uses two other German agents, GA (Tabun) and GD (Soman). However, British and U.S. scientists have developed a new nerve agent — the V agent — and the U.S. refined this to produce VX which, with its oily texture, is highly persistent and lethal in doses of less than half a milligram.

The distinction between persistent and non-persistent agents is important. The latter will evaporate in a short time and can be used on the battlefields to support quick tactical thrusts, whereas the former will render whole areas thus treated unusable for days.

The future of chemical weapons is closely linked with genetic developments and there are suggestions that agents could be developed which would attack certain ethnic groups, since they would be the only people with the correct genetic characteristics to be vulnerable on the battlefield. Black women, for example, would lack the chromosomes which make most NATO soldiers vulnerable to the weapon. In a frightening scenario the genetically tailored device could be employed covertly by one nation against another to attack a whole male generation and destroy that nation's social system.

Perhaps the greatest danger of binary weapons, however, is that they fall into a gray area in arms limitation talks. Nuclear and chemical warheads can be counted physically and their numbers and deployment agreed by treaty: not so binary weapons which consist, in their simplest form, of two piles of innocuous chemicals some distance apart. Unless binary weapons become the subject of a special treaty aimed at limiting the production of the two chemical agents, there is very little that can be done to prevent an horrific proliferation of these deadly killers.

Amphibious vehicle

Amphibious vehicles, which can travel both on land and in water under their own power, range from specially adapted tanks to various designs of home-built swamp buggies.

Amphibious craft are mainly used for two purposes – pleasure and warfare. Farmers and foresters in wild country also make use of the versatility and toughness that they offer.

The current trend in nonmilitary amphibians is toward All Terrain Vehicles (ATVs). Mostly U.S. and Canadian built, they are usually based on two essential components: fat, ribbed tires at very low pressures, and a transmission system using belts and tapered pulleys that adjusts the speed automatically according to the throttle setting. The softness of the tire, with pressures as low as 0.1 bar, lets the tread spread out to give maximum traction on land. The variable transmission relieves the driver of changing gear in normal forward use. Conventional gears are used for reverse, and in some cases to give high and low speed ranges too. From the transmission onward the mechanical principles are the same on most ATVs – an output pulley is mounted on a cross-shaft terminating at each end in clutch plates which transmit the drive to the wheels on both sides of the vehicle. To steer the vehicle, one of the clutches on these drive shafts is disengaged and comes in contact with a disc brake to slow down the wheels on one side.

Most ATVs have six or eight wheels, which steer and drive them in water as well as on land. The vehicles' light weight and low CENTER OF GRAVITY enable them to climb steep slopes easily and safely and the big soft tires mold easily round obstacles. Engines are usually single cylinder units of around 15 cu in. (250 cc).

A typical ATV is the Amphicat. It has a tough, lightweight plastic body and is powered by a Curtiss-Wright single cylinder, two stroke, air-cooled engine. It has expanding pulley and chain transmission with a high, low and reverse range gearbox. A six wheeler, it weighs 400 lb (180 kg) and can carry 480 lb (220 kg).

Below: The ¼ ton 4x4 Model GPA Amphibian was an extensive modification of the familar Jeep, and was in use with U.S. forces in World War II.

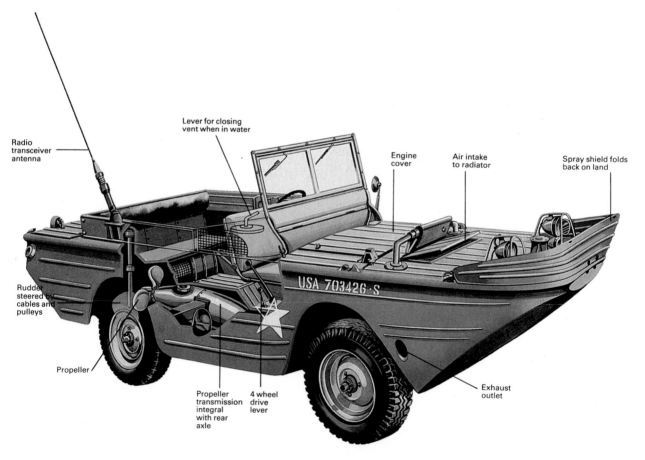

Radio transceiver antenna

Lever for closing vent when in water

Engine cover

Air intake to radiator

Spray shield folds back on land

Rudder steered by cables and pulleys

Propeller

Propeller transmission integral with rear axle

4 wheel drive lever

Exhaust outlet

USA 703426·S

Above: The U.S. LARC–5 amphibian is a direct descendant of the DUKW and GPA vehicles, and is a four wheel drive type that floats in deep water.

Some ATVs have an articulated body, consisting of two separate watertight hulls that can move independently of each other in response to the terrain to keep all the wheels constantly in contact with the ground. The U.S.-built Twister is such a vehicle. Others employ tanklike rubber tracks.

The problems of transport in the Everglades swamps of Florida led to the development of another type of amphibian, the swamp buggy. Swamp buggies ride on large truck, tractor or aircraft tires which support and drive them through thick mud and water.

More eccentric attempts at amphibians include an amphibious bicycle, shown at Lyons, France in 1909. The front fork was linked by a rod to a rudder, and a small friction wheel at the rear drove a propeller. Cylindrical floats attached to the frame could be raised or lowered as required.

There have been several attempts at converting ordinary road vehicles into temporary amphibians; essentially cheap alternatives to bridges or ferries. A current one, built in New Zealand, consists of a floating platform onto which an automobile or truck is driven. The front wheels hang through slots into the water and act as rudders. The driving wheels rest on rubber-covered rollers which power twin propellers through a friction drive mechanism. Reverse gear provides a brake. Other similar devices have used simple rear mounted paddles.

The advance of the air cushion vehicle (hovercraft) is reducing demand for amphibians. Most dual drive amphibians waste time when transferring from water to land and vice versa because they have to pause while the switch is made to another propulsion method. Indeed, there are few amphibians with very good performance on both land and water, this being the price of their versatility.

Military vehicles

Military amphibians fall into several clear groups. First, and on the most basic level, are those that are primarily land vehicles that have the need to take to the water for the purpose of beach landings or river crossings. Next are those land vehicles that have built-in buoyancy by virtue of their design and are capable of making limited passages without special preparation. Finally, there are surface effect craft (hovercraft) which are more at home on the water but fully capable of overland transit.

Of the first group, all are negatively buoyant and need preparation either to give them enough temporary buoyancy to float or to create the ability to crawl along the sea or river bed. Techniques for floating tanks ashore are as old as the major landings of World War II. It is essential, of course, that the main hull of the vehicle can be made watertight, with all protruding shafts sealed at their exit

Below: The heavily armored U.S. LVTP–7, popularly called the Amtrack, is capable of transporting a payload of 19 personnel and their equipment.

points. A steel platform can then be welded around the upper hull and a waterproof screen raised from it, supported by pneumatic tubes inflated by compressed air supply from the vehicle. No special water propulsion unit is provided, forward thrust being generated by running the wheels or tracks, which act as paddlewheels.

What might be termed bottom-crawling is very common, particularly in Soviet practice, for the negotiation of the many large river barriers in continental Europe. No attempt is made to float the vehicle, it being sufficient to erect a vertical tube from the turret hatch sufficiently high to project above the surface (that on the French AMX 30 tank, for instance, is 15 ft (4.6 m) in length). The tank commander stands within the top and gives instruc-

Far left, top: A Combat Engineer tractor armored amphibian support vehicle. The vehicle can perform a variety of roles, from digging gun emplacements to clearing obstacles from roads or beaches.

Far left, below: British Army M amphibious bridging rigs on maneuvers. These rigs have stacked decking which is lifted across by gantries and coupled together to form bridge sections.

Left top: U.S. Tracked Landing Vehicles (LVTs) coming ashore during an exercise. The LVT is driven on both land and water by tracks equipped with W-shaped protuberances (grousers) to give greater thrust. LVTs can cope with both heavy surf and rocky beaches with equal ease.

Left center: LVTs, carrying between 25 and 30 occupants, are beached as troops deploy out. These vehicles weight about 38 tons when fully laden, and are 30 ft long, 12 ft wide, and 10 ft high.

Left bottom: Control center of the amphibious command ship U.S.S. Mount Whitney, a vessel of post World War II. Amphibious assault ships within its command can carry up to 1500 troops, plus amphibious vehicles, aircraft, helicopters, and missiles – a formidable attack force.

The second group, the truly amphibious vehicles are, paradoxically, becoming less common by virtue of the development of the third, the surface-effect craft. Most are thin-skinned and for personnel or cargo transport, but modern armor can be made from aluminum, plastic or a sandwich of both, the result being of low enough density to permit the building of a buoyant tank. Such is the Soviet PT-76, which incorporates also a water-jet propulsion unit, which is fairly common and obviates the need for the complexities of shafts and propellers.

The Duck

The doyen of amphibious vehicles is the familiar Duck. More correctly the DUKW (Duplex Universal Karrier, Wheeled), it was introduced in 1942 by General Motors as a development of their standard 6 x 6 truck chassis – six wheels, all driven. Topsides it pioneered the boat-shaped hull which, once afloat, was propelled by a marine propeller, clutched in as an alternative to the wheel drive. Its speeds of 50 mph (80 km/h) on land and 6 mph (10 km/h) afloat are little exceeded by current examples; indeed, many of these are so like the original that the basic design cannot be questioned.

Modern derivatives range greatly in size from the little Soviet GAZ-46, a 4 x 4 (four wheels, all driven) with a useful payload of 1100 lb (500 kg), enabling it to transport a patrol of five personnel, to the giant U.S. LARC-60. Another 4 x 4, this vehicle is 60 ft (19 m) in length, weighing 37 tons (37,000 kg) empty and capable of floating with a payload of 60 tons (60,000 kg), though this can be considerably

tions to the crew below. Also necessary, of course, is a snort system, a temporary double pipe taking air down for running the engine and providing a route for its exhaust. This method can also be used to allow vehicles to transmit from landing craft to the beach where, say, an offshore bar prevents a close approach; the bottom must not be deeply rilled or the surf too heavy, or the vehicles may be swamped.

Above: A German Panzer Mk 3 tank during World War II. Fitted with a snorkel attached to the air intake filter, it could cross a river totally submerged.

exceeded in an emergency. LARC-60 stands for Lighter, Amphibious, Resupply, Cargo, 60-ton, it being designed primarily to act as a ferry between the beach and ships lying offshore. It can offload its cargo directly on to the beach via its own bowramp or it can take the ground, engage the wheel drive and progress inland still loaded. Each wheel is powered by a separate engine, the pair of engines on each side being capable of driving one of two marine propellers, set into tunnels below the hull.

Although most amphibians are wheeled, some, such as the Soviet PTS, are tracked, improving their mobility in difficult conditions once ashore. Wheeled vehicles in difficult conditions commonly reduce their tire pressures to improve traction.

Surface-effect vehicles are unlikely to replace the more conventional wheeled or tracked amphibians completely, but they are becoming more numerous in a variety of configurations and can be built many times larger than even the LARC-60. Rigid sidewall craft with conventional diesel/propeller propulsion are not truly amphibious; for progress ashore hovercraft need an aircraft type propeller and flexible or combination skirts. Once ashore, its low air cushion limits its ability to negotiate the type of obstacle that would also hinder more conventional vehicles but it will progress easily over marsh, deep snow, thin ice or rapidly flowing water that would be otherwise impassable. Its size can be large because, unlike a wheeled vehicle, it is supported elastically over its complete bottom by its air cushion. For instance, the British Hovercraft Corporation's non-military SRN4 Mk 3 Super Four can transport up to 60 standard cars and over 400 passengers. It has a maximum speed of about 65 knots (120 km/h) and can cruise for about 4½ hours and would need little modification to be militarized.

The Soviets in particular have recognized the hovercraft's potential in an assault role, their Lebed being typical. This is a 60-knot (110 km/h) craft with a 35-ton payload, enough to lift a brace of the PT-76 tanks mentioned above. Like many more orthodox landing craft, they are dimensioned to fit snugly into the well of an amphibious assault ship, such as an LPD. Thus, the recently introduced Soviet Ivan Rogov class of ship can accommodate three preloaded Lebeds.

See also: Air cushion vehicle; Automobile; Marine propulsion; Rudder; Ship; Tank.

Amplifier

An amplifier is a device for increasing or magnifying the strength of a force or a signal. Amplification is one of the most commonly applied scientific principles, because there is need for amplifiers in every branch of technology.

In the early days of electronics, amplification was achieved by the use of thermionic valves. Today, these have been displaced by TRANSISTORS except for some high-power applications, for example, in broadcasting transmitters. The transistor can perform amplification, so it is called an *active* device. Two transistors together with RESISTORS, CAPACITORS and a direct current (DC) voltage supply are sufficient for a complete amplifier stage, several of which might be employed in a medium-priced radio or hi-fi system. Each stage provides an amplification or gain.

Some stages have a negative gain, the value of which is less than one. In these, the output signal is less than the input, but the gain of most stages is positive – greater than one. A gain of 20, or an output signal 20 times the strength of the input, is considered low, whereas a gain of 200 is not uncommon. The overall gain of an amplifier can be extremely large. For example, two stages each with a gain of 100 would produce an overall gain 100 x 100 = 10,000. Hence it is usual to measure gain in decibels (dB), which avoids the need for these inconveniently large numbers. Expressed in decibels, a gain of 10 equals 20 dB, and a gain of 10,000 equals 80 dB.

The amplifying action of a transistor depends upon the arrangement of its two junctions, one between the *base* and *emitter* terminals, the other between the *collector* and emitter terminals. When a small AC signal or voltage (say from a radio antenna or a phonograph pickup) is applied to the base, a small current flows in the base-emitter circuit. The small current causes a much larger current to flow through the collector-emitter junction and into the collector-emitter circuit. If the collector-emitter current is passed through a *load* resistor it develops across the load a voltage which is a much amplified copy of the input signal. The transistor stage has amplified the input signal or applied voltage, and the output can then be passed to another stage for further amplification.

The capacitors in the circuit allow AC signals to flow through them, but block or prevent DC from flowing. The energy or power in the amplified signal comes from the DC power source, which every amplifier requires. So the transistor is an energy converter, converting DC energy from the power source into energy which is usually used to increase the input signal.

In a *field effect* transistor (FET), there are similar

AMPLIFIER CIRCUIT

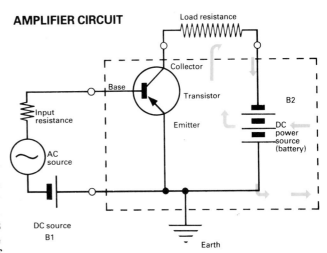

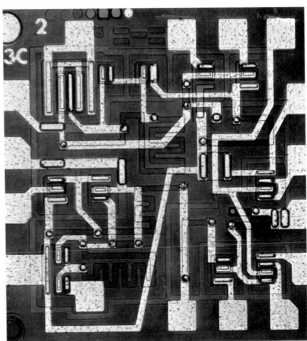

Top: Diagrammatical representation of a simple amplifier circuit. The signal voltage to be amplified is fed in from left to the base-emitter circuit.
Above: Integrated circuit containing all amplifier stage components in a microchip.

pairs of junctions, but the terminals are labeled differently. Instead of a base, an emitter and a collector, there is a *gate*, a *source* and a *drain*. One junction is between the gate and source and the other is between the drain and source. The difference between FETs and other transistors is that FETs need only an electric field, not a current, at the gate-source junction to cause a large current flow across the drain-source junction. For this reason, FETs can produce far greater amplification, and they have almost negligible input requirements.

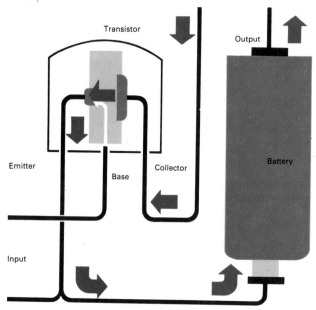

Above: This stereo amplifier unit contains both the preamplifier and the power amplifier stages and has a power output of 110 watts.

Amplifiers in practice

An audio amplifier is designed first to raise the tiny signal voltages from a radio tuner, pickup cartridge or tape recording head to levels that can be adjusted, say by the volume or tone controls, so allowing the signal to be modified before it is heard. These voltages, which are higher but have little power, are then turned into high electric power for driving the loudspeakers. The two tasks are sometimes done by separate amplifiers – the *preamplifier* and the *power amplifier* – or sometimes they are combined in one unit, called an *integrated* amplifier. A small, budget audio system might have an amplifier producing about 20 watts of electric power for each stereo channel, whereas a system of the highest quality might produce about 100 watts per channel or considerably more.

Ideally, an amplifier in a radio, television or hi-fi system should produce an accurate, though greatly amplified, copy of the original input signal, preserving every detail of, say, a complex music signal in exact proportion. No amplifier is perfect, however, and several techniques are used in design to make the amplifier as accurate as possible, hence the term high fidelity – the finest quality.

One of the problems always associated with amplifiers is *noise*. This loose term covers a number of phenomena, but the most familiar is the rush or hiss that can be sometimes heard in the background when the amplifier is switched on but not operating, or the inter-station noise of a radio tuner. These sounds result from the steady current flow from the DC sources through the components – the *quiescent current* – and can never be eliminated. The use of FET devices, however, is one factor that can further reduce noise because FETs require such small currents to operate them.

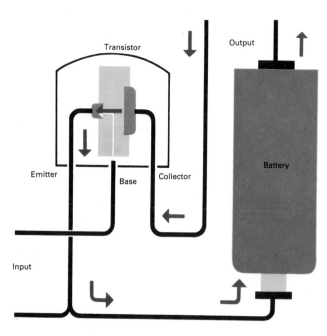

Above: How a circuit works. When the current to the transistor base emitter is large, the collector-emitter circuit current is larger.

The junctions of transistors and other active devices are extremely small, and it has become possible to integrate many of them, including the resistors and capacitors, onto a single substrate or chip. Integrated circuits allow several amplifying stages to be incorporated into one device or package, with the advantage that the complete amplifier takes up little space. Sophisticated electronic circuits can be miniaturized, as in today's desktop or even book-sized home computers.

Top left: Amplifier units are produced to meet the wide variety of applications with the performance characteristics of the amplifier being closely matched to the job which it has to perform. Bottom left: With public address (PA) systems the amplifier section is often built into a cabinet along with the loudspeaker unit to give an integrated assembly that can be quickly manhandled onto the stage and connected up ready for a performance. Adjustment of the sound output to meet the different acoustic characteristics of venues may be achieved by the use of independent amplifier and loudspeaker combinations to handle individual sections of the frequency spectrum.

Another problem with amplifiers is that they may not amplify the incoming signal in exact proportion, but produce some distortion. This is especially critical in the later stages where high signal levels are handled. The solution to this is *negative feedback*, a technique which returns (feeds back) a small proportion of the output signal from the amplifier to its input, in a negative sense. The feedback can be used to cancel any distortion the amplifier may have introduced. Applying negative feedback, which most amplifiers feature, reduces the overall gain, but this is easily restored in the earlier stages where distortion is less likely to occur. Negative feedback also makes the amplifier less susceptible to variations between transistors of the same type and also

to circuit component tolerances which can be due to overheating.

A high-quality audio amplifier covers the audible frequency range from about 20 Hz to 20,000 Hz, produces distortion of no more than about 0.2 per cent, and has a signal-to-noise ratio of at least 70 dB. This range of frequencies is known as the *bandwidth*. A television signal needs a much wider frequency range than an audio amplifier, because the picture signal is far more detailed. Video amplifiers used in domestic television sets, for example, have bandwidths typically of from 0 to 6 MHz (6 million Hz).

See also: Electronics; Capacitor; Hi-fi system; Loudspeaker; Radio; Resistor; Sound; Transistor.

Anemometer

Strictly speaking, anemometers are instruments for measuring wind speed, but their use has also been extended to the measurement of fluid velocities.

The type of anemometer used depends on the nature of the fluid, the range of velocities likely to be encountered and the accuracy required. For the measurement of wind speeds, however, there are essentially three types of anemometer: the cup, propeller and pitot-static pressure tube.

Cup anemometer

The simplest type of wind speed indicator is the rotating cup anemometer. This consists of three or four conical or hemispherical cups mounted at the ends of horizontal spokes which radiate from a vertical rotating shaft. The concave surfaces of the cups offer greater wind resistance than their convex surfaces, causing them to catch the wind efficiently and rotate.

When the wind is steady, the cups rotate at a speed approximating to that of the wind. By attaching a revolution counter to the shaft and counting the number of revolutions in a certain period, the wind speed can be calculated quite accurately.

Alternatively, a continuous indication of the rate of rotation (and hence the wind speed) can be achieved by coupling a small dynamo to the shaft. This produces a voltage output proportional to the rate of rotation and the wind speeds can then be read directly off a suitably calibrated voltmeter.

In gusty winds, the cup anemometer tends to overrate the average wind speed because the rotating cups speed up at a faster rate than they slow down and this can produce over-running errors as high as 30 per cent. Nevertheless, it is a simple and inexpensive device capable of measuring wind speeds from 5 to 100 mph (8 to 160 km/h).

Propeller anemometer

Propeller anemometers are suitable for the measurement of low air speeds in the region of 1 to 25 mph (1 to 40 km/h). In this case blades of a propeller, or fan, are attached to a horizontal rotating shaft directed into the wind by a weathervanelike tail fin. The speed of rotation is proportional to the wind speed and can be measured by the same methods as used with cup anemometers.

Mechanical anemometers cannot be accurately calibrated simply from their dimensions, since factors such as friction vary from instrument to instrument. They must, therefore, be calibrated in the controlled conditions of a wind tunnel, the air speed being measured by a pressure anemometer.

Pitot-static anemometer

The pitot-static pressure tube anemometer is mechanically simple, having no moving parts, and has many applications, both wind tunnels and aircraft employing them as air speed indicators.

The main part is a probe consisting of two separate tubes aligned into the wind. The pitot tube is open at one end, allowing air to blow in and hence cause a pressure build-up. The pressure is the sum of the static air pressure and the dynamic produced by the flow of air into the tube.

The other tube is the static tube, closed and rounded at its upstream end with a series of holes around the tube some distance downstream. The airstream is effectively undisturbed by the rounded front of the static tube, so this tube contains air at the static pressure alone.

Between the downstream ends of the tubes there is a differential pressure gauge. This measures the pressure difference between the two tubes, thus giving the dynamic pressure of the pitot tube.

Pitot-static anemometers cause some disturbance in the airstream and so are not suitable for velocity measurements in confined spaces where such disturbances may be significant.

See also: **Airport; Friction; Hydrodynamics; Meteorology; Pitot tube; Pressure; Wind tunnel.**

Left: Checking the rate of airflow from an air conditioning outlet with a portable, electronic rotating vane (or propeller) anemometer.

Anesthetic

Anesthetic machines are used to induce a temporary state of unconsciousness in a patient undergoing an operation – and with the complicated surgery being performed today, that may mean keeping the patient unconscious for many hours.

The machine supplies the patient's lungs with a mixture of anesthetic gases which are selected by the anesthetist according to the degree of unconsciousness required, the health or age of the patient, and the type of surgery being performed. Under anesthetic, the patient should be insensitive to pain and have no muscular reflexes which could interfere with the surgeon's delicate manipulations.

Nitrous oxide (N_2O) and cyclopropane (C_3H_6) are gases commonly used for inhalation anesthesia, supplied together with oxygen (O_2) via a mask and a tube inserted through the mouth and into the throat.

Nitrous oxide is a nonflammable gas, stored as a liquid compressed into cylinders and used as the sole anesthetic agent in most dentistry. Because the gas is not irritating to the lungs, it is often used to induce unconsciousness before introducing a more pungent anesthetic such as ether when the patient is well and truly under.

Cyclopropane is stored as a liquid in low-pressure cylinders. It is extremely potent, highly explosive, and is only used in concentrations of up to 20 per cent in oxygen to induce anesthesia.

Liquid anesthetic agents, such as ether and halothane, are also widely used. But to make them breathable, they must first be broken into droplets

Below: The anesthetist must keep a constant check on the proportions of the gas mixture fed to the patient during the course of a surgical operation.

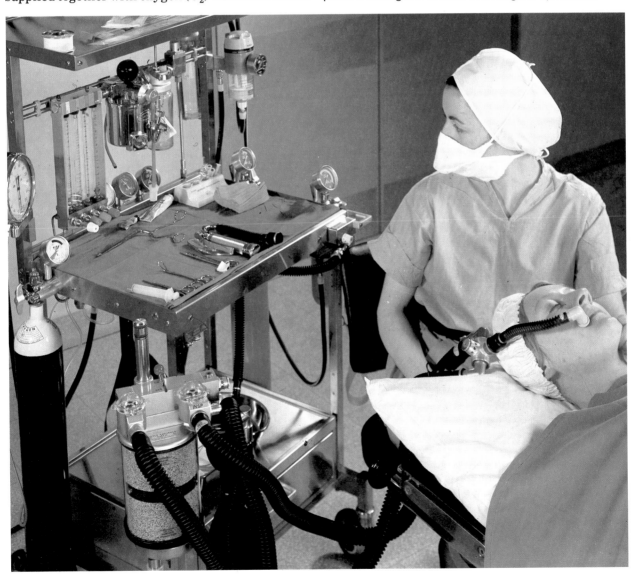

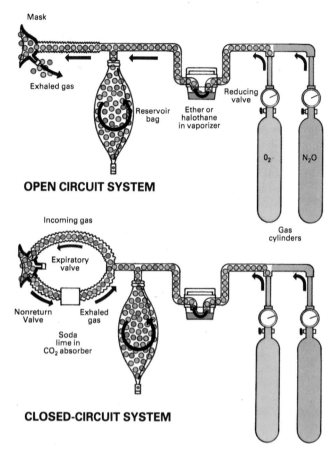

OPEN CIRCUIT SYSTEM

Mask

Exhaled gas

Reservoir bag

Ether or halothane in vaporizer

Reducing valve

O_2 N_2O

Gas cylinders

CLOSED-CIRCUIT SYSTEM

Incoming gas

Expiratory valve

Nonreturn Valve

Exhaled gas

Soda lime in CO_2 absorber

Above: In the open-circuit type of anesthetic machine the exhaled gases are vented to the air, whereas in a closed system they are chemically scrubbed.

by a vaporizer in the machine. Trichloroethylene vapor is another popular gas.

Design of machines

The most basic anesthetic machine is *Boyle's apparatus*, introduced in 1917 and still very widely used, in a much improved form. The components are usually either supported on a moveable trolley, or installed conveniently close to the operating table.

Gas is supplied from cylinders attached to the machine or by hoses from a bulk supply in another part of the hospital. In this case, the machine may have cylinders as a standby for use in emergencies. The normal complement of cylinders is two of oxygen (colored black with a white top, for easy identification), two of nitrous oxide (blue), one of carbon dioxide (gray), and one small cylinder of cyclopropane (orange). Carbon dioxide (CO_2) is included for use as a stimulant, should breathing become weak during the operation.

Each type of cylinder and its accompanying hose has connections of different designs to prevent attachment to the wrong inlet. Reducing valves are fitted to the high-pressure O_2, CO_2 and N_2O cylinders to supply the gases at a suitably low pressure. Cyclopropane, however, is already at the correct pressure and can be fed directly into the machine from its storage cylinder.

The selected gases are fed separately into *flowmeters*, which indicate the quantities of each in the mixture being delivered to the patient. These flowmeters are tapered tubes, containing loosely fitting plungers. The plunger floats on the gas as it passes up through the tube, a more rapid flow being required to carry it to the top, where the tube is widest. The height of the plunger on the scale indicates the flow rate.

When vapor from liquid anesthetics is to be added to the mixture, the combined gas flow is directed through a vaporizer. This is a container holding liquid ether, halothane, or trichloroethylene, which evaporates as the gas mixture is blown across the surface, or bubbled through it. From the vaporizer, the mixture passes to a rubber reservoir bag. This fills with gas, then deflates as the patient inhales, refilling while the patient exhales.

The final anesthetic mixture passes along a wide corrugated rubber tube to the mask, which is held over the patient's face. An expiratory valve is fitted to the mask to prevent exhaled gases being forced back into the incoming mixture, which would cause carbon dioxide build-up and eventual suffocation. Exhaled gases leaving the expiratory valve are often ducted out of the operating room.

A tube called a *pharyngal airway* is often passed into the patient's throat to prevent the tongue from obstructing gas flow to the lungs. In the more complex closed-circuit systems, exhaled gases are not exhausted from the apparatus, but pass through a cylinder containing soda lime (a mixture of sodium hydroxide and lime), which absorbs the carbon dioxide, then they pass back into the reservoir bag, from which the mixture is reinhaled.

If the patient's respiration is inhibited by deep anesthesia, or by the use of muscle relaxant drugs, a *ventilator* may be used to assist breathing. This is a rubber bellows which pumps the gas mixture into the lungs automatically, the patient exhaling normally. There are, however, various models of highly sophisticated, automatic ventilators, some of which are specifically for either adults or children. In addition, there are instruments that monitor the ventilator's output and raise an alarm should be malfunction occur. This information, together with readings of blood pressure, pulse rate and various other factors monitored on separate machines, is available to the modern anesthetist at all times throughout an operation.

See also: Ambulance; Drug; Electronics in medicine; Flowmeter; Operating room; Surgery.

Angle

Angles are one of the basic constituents of much of geometry. The ancient Greek philospher, Euclid, wrote 13 books on geometry, called his Elements. These were the groundwork for Pure Geometry, which stood virtually unchallenged from Euclid's lifetime (approximately 300 BC) until the developments in science and mathematics during the nineteenth century which led up to Einstein's great reworking of scientific thought. It was not until early this century that a selected part of Euclid's Elements was discarded from school mathematics text books, where it normally appeared virtually unaltered. Although angles have their origin somewhere in ancient Greek thought, the term angle comes from the Latin *angulus,* meaning corner.

Angles and planes

An angle is formed where two *lines* or two *planes* meet. Before a line or a plane can be defined, geometry's definition of a *point* needs to be understood. A point is simply a position in space — it has no dimensions, just a location. A line, or more correctly, a *straight line* is the result of joining two points by the shortest distance. A plane is defined as a surface on which, if any two points are taken, the straight line joining them will lie entirely within that surface.

Despite this definition sounding extremely abstract, what angles are is quite self-evident – everyone knows what an angle is almost intuitively. People understand the concept of straight lines, and that they meet to form angles.

The point at which two lines meet is called the *vertex* of the angle, and the lines themselves are sometimes called the *legs, sides* or *arms* of the angle.

Rotation

The size of an angle is often thought of by mathematicians as the amount of rotation that one of the two arms has made. Imagine that one of the arms is fixed, but the other may rotate like a hand of a clock.

In some kinds of geometry, mathematicians like to differentiate between clockwise and counterclockwise rotation. The fixed arm is usually called an *axis*. Axes have special properties which will be dealt with later. Angles formed by clockwise rotation away from an axis are termed *positive* angles, while angles formed by counterclockwise rotation are termed *negative* angles.

Measuring angles

Angles are measured in either *radians* or *degrees*. A complete rotation is defined as 2π radians; a straight line – half a revolution – is defined as π radians. It is usual to define and/or measure angles in this system in terms of multiples or fractions of π – π being a number which is approximately 3.142, but is a constant associated with circles, and was originally discovered by the ancient Greeks.

If an angle is measured in degrees, the quantities are different. A complete revolution is defined as 360°, and a straight line is defined as 180°.

Angles greater than 2π radians or 360° are allowed in some kinds of geometry – such as rotary motion – which have arms which rotate many times. Negative angles may be from 0 radians or degrees to an infinity of radians or degrees, by rotating the arm counterclockwise.

Below: Angles come into everyday life in a variety of ways. They are the basis of all building and essential in height and distance measurement.

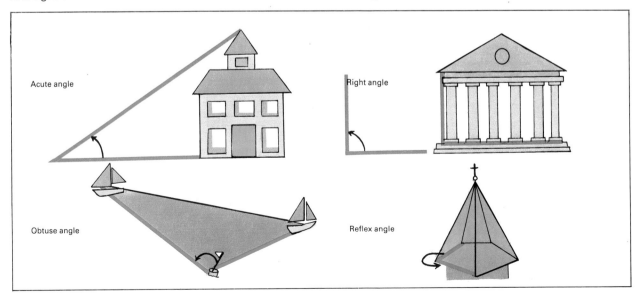

Acute angle

Obtuse angle

Right angle

Reflex angle

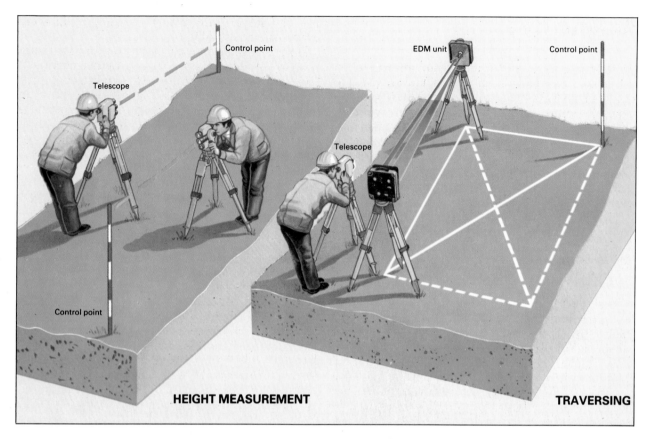

HEIGHT MEASUREMENT

TRAVERSING

Above: Determining the difference in height between two control points using a telescope. By using the traversing technique (above right) surveyors can quickly measure distance.

Naming angles

An angle of $\pi/2$ radians or 90° is called a *right angle*. There are four right angles in a complete rotation; a right angle is to be found in each corner of a square. An angle of π radians or 180° is called a *straight angle* for obvious reasons.

Other angles are named according to the range of sizes that they fall into. An *acute angle* is any angle between 0 and $\pi/2$ radians, or between 0 and 90°. Angles between $\pi/2$ and π radians or between 90° and 180° are called *obtuse angles*. Angles between π and 2π radians or between 180° and 360° are called *reflex angles*.

If the result of adding two angles is $\pi/2$ radians or 90°, the angles are called *complementary angles*. Angles are *supplementary* if their sum is π radians or 180°.

Triangles, squares and polygons

Triangles, squares and polygons are geometrical figures, with varying numbers of angles – the word *polygon* comes from the Greek meaning many angles. Triangles have three angles, squares four, and polygons more than four.

Trigonometry

Trigonometry is the branch of geometry dealing with the relationship between the sides and angles of triangles – normally *right angled* triangles; those with one $\pi/2$ radian or 90° angle.

There are six ratios of sides used in trigonometry. These are *sine, cosine, tangent, secant, cosecant,* and *cotangent*. Using these ratios, the lengths of particular sides or the sizes of angles can be calculated if you know the length of two sides, or the length of one side and the size of an angle. Standard tables of these ratios are widely available, calculated for different angles.

Trigonometry has many applications, not least in surveying. For example, it is easy to find the height of a tall building without measuring it. If the surveyor stands a known distant from the building and uses a theodolite to measure the *angle of elevation* from where he is standing, either *tangent* or *cotangent* can be used to calculate the height:

Height of the building = distance surveyor is standing from building x tan (angle measured).

Similarly, distance is determined by a method known as traversing.

See also: Building techniques; Mathematics; Rangefinder; Road construction; Surveying.

Aniline dye

Until the mid-nineteenth century, humans had relied on natural dyestuffs such as madder (a red dye known to the Egyptians as early as 1500 BC), indigo (blue), cochineal (scarlet) and saffron (yellow). Eventually, rapid advances in chemistry made the development of synthetic dyes inevitable. As sometimes happens in research, however, new materials came to light purely by chance.

In the first half of the nineteenth century, France and Britain dominated the chemicals industry with materials such as sulfuric acid, sodium hydroxide and chlorine. It was, however, the Germans who were to become the leading discoverers in ORGANIC CHEMISTRY. By the end of the nineteenth century, this expertise had made them world leaders in the manufacture of dyes and medicines, thanks to the early influence of researchers such as Liebig, Wöhler, Bunsen and Hofmann. They were such inspiring teachers that many of their pupils carried out experiments with makeshift apparatus at home, and Hofmann was invited to Britain to help establish the Royal College of Chemistry in London, which opened in 1845.

Hofmann was particularly interested in the substances found in coal tar. Having studied aniline in 1843, he went on to prepare it from nitrobenzene. He obtained this by isolating benzene and then treating it with nitric acid. A group of aniline-type COMPOUNDS was discovered, one of which, allyl-toluidine, appeared to be similar to quinine – the important compound obtained from the bark of a Peruvian tree and used to treat malaria.

In 1856, one of Hofmann's pupils, William Perkins, aged 18, tried to synthesize quinine from allyl-toluidine. Disappointingly, he produced only a reddish-brown sludge. He repeated the experiment, with aniline as the basis, and prepared a black sludge, part of which dissolved in water to give a mauve color. Intrigued by the color, he tried dyeing a piece of silk. So successful was the result that he

Left: August Wilhelm Hofmann, a nineteenth century German chemist who was the first to prepare aniline from nitrobenzene by isolating benzene and treating it with nitric acid.
Below: Natural dyes produce mellow red and browns.

immediately patented the discovery – the first synthetic dye. Assisted by his father and brother he went into commercial production within six months, building a factory at Greenford Green, in northwest London.

The breakthrough having been made, it was not long before more aniline dyes were synthesized; fuchsine or rosaniline, a deep rose pink color discovered by Nantaston in 1856, was made in 1859 by Verquin by heating commercial aniline with tin tetrachloride. By this time, the range of colors had increased to include Hofmann's violet, methyl violet, iodide green and Nicholson's blue. At the same time Peter Griess, a German working for a brewery in Britain spent his spare time studying azo (nitrogen) compounds and discovered the diazonium salts, which were used to synthesize a new range of dyes, red, yellow and orange; these were not developed commercially until the late 1870s. During this period, another range of dyes was discovered, by Baeyer. These are the phthaleins, which are red. Then in the 1890s, the sulfur dyes (black, brown and yellow) were synthesized.

The development of the pharmaceutical industry was slower than that of the dye industry but because Perkin had initially sought a medicine and not a dye, both industries have been closely linked. Paul Ehrlich, noting the property of dyes selectively to stain different types of tissue or microorganisms such as bacteria, tried to discover if dyes had any therapeutic effect on diseases. A red diazo dye was known to attack sleeping sickness germs, but being toxic, it was only suitable for treating extreme cases. Experiments with other dyes led to the discovery in 1909 of Salvarsan, which had the nitrogen link of the dye molecule replaced by arsenic, and was used to treat syphilis.

Domagk and his team also investigated the therapeutic properties of dyes, and in the 1930s came up with the famous sulfanilamide drugs, so effective against the deadly streptococci which causes blood poisoning.

See also: Clothing manufacture; Dyeing process; Fabric printing; Organic chemistry; Textile.

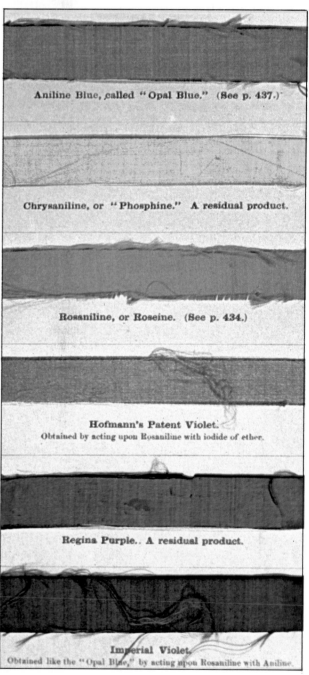

Aniline Blue, called "Opal Blue." (See p. 437.)

Chrysaniline, or "Phosphine." A residual product.

Rosaniline, or Roseine. (See p. 434.)

Hofmann's Patent Violet.
Obtained by acting upon Rosaniline with iodide of ether.

Regina Purple.. A residual product.

Imperial Violet.
Obtained like the "Opal Blue," by acting upon Rosaniline with Aniline.

Above: A selection of early synthetic dyes which enabled clothing manufacturers to produce brightly colored new ranges. Left: The first synthetic dye factory in London was the enterprise of William Perkin who discovered the process in 1856.